THE BIG DUMMY'S GUIDE TO C.B. RADIO

D1244669

The Book Publishing Company — Summertown, Tennessee 38483

Inspired by the Ranger, who helped us all get out.

Publisher: The Publisher (Paul Mandelstein)

Editors:
White Lightning AB4BWR (Albert Houston)
Stringbean AA4LXC (Mark Long)
Minnesota Mumbler AB4KDH (Jeffrey Keating)
Ratchet Jaw AD4IAP (William Hershfield)
Buffalo Bill AA4KCF (William Brady)

Artists:
Midnight Artist (Mark Schlichting)
Mister Fixit (Peter Hoyt)

Thanks to all the other Big Dummies
whose help made this book possible.

All members of the KHT 1296 group.

TABLE OF CONTENTS

BREAK! ONE-NINE.

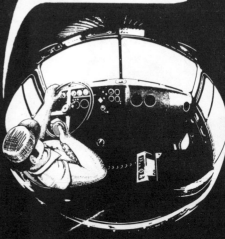

BRING IT ON...

"WHAT'S YOUR HANDLE THERE BUDDY?"

"YOU GOT THE LEADFOOT HERE — WHO I GOT THERE?"

YOU GOT ONE FROGMAN HERE. YOU IN THAT 18 WHEELER UP AHEAD THERE LEADFOOT?

There's all kinds of folks getting into CB radio nowadays. CB radio has really become the people's radio service. It offers free communications for anyone who wants it, and you don't have to know a lot of fancy radio theory to get on the air. There's an estimated ten million CB radios in service right now. You can even get them factory equipped in some new automobiles. So you might have ended up with a rig and not know much about how to use it or how it works. Or maybe you're interested in getting a CB but don't know where to start. In the first few chapters we discuss buying a rig, getting it set up to work, and talking on it. Also we'll give you some simple explanations about how they work. If you're an old time CBer and have had a rig for awhile, there are some interesting ideas a little later in the book.

CB communication is not only fun, but it's smart too. On the interstate, back home, or in the office, CB is a useful tool for almost anyone. Truck drivers and motorists and the highway patrol use CB to keep things together on the road. It gives them an extra sense that stretches them on out miles ahead on the interstates and highways, so that they can perceive changing road conditions, weather, accidents, and other driving hazards. Truck drivers use CB as a means of staying intelligent behind the fast paced, hammer-down lifeline of America.

CB radio offers a means of staying connected with your business. For many people, the added communication means added gain, too. CB communications add an extra means of being in the right place at the right time.

CB radio also lets you talk to your home from your mobile via the radio airways. It's convenient for saving time at stops, sending instructions, and relaying important phone calls and messages, as well as helping you stay connected to your family.

In an emergency, CB radio may be the only means of getting help. There are emergency groups (HELP, REACT, etc.) into CB that monitor the radio and can offer help and assistance. These folks also help in times of natural disaster. Many local police and state troopers are getting CBs, too, making them more readily available to motorists when needed.

CHAPTER 1

Getting on the Air

Basic Modjitating

A CB radio is technically called a transceiver, which is a combination of a transmitter and receiver. Your car radio is a receiver that you can listen to—but you can't talk back to the DJ. CB radio can be more fun than an AM radio, because you get to communicate with the folks that you hear. Throughout the book we use CB, CB radio, rig, transmitter, hunk of junk, chicken box, squawk box, and the like, interchangeably with the words "Citizen's Band radio."

Modulating

Well, you can't actually hear the radio waves themselves. Your voice is hooked onto the radio waves by a process called modulation. Modulating also means talking on your CB. We use modulate, modjitate, and ratchet jawing to mean the same thing. When you first get a rig you could give a listen for a while to get a feel for what's going on. If you want to jump right in there, though, don't worry—the other folks on the channel will let you know how you're doing. CB is a down-home mode of communication and folks will love modulating with you. If you don't understand all the lingo, check out our glossary on Channel Jive.

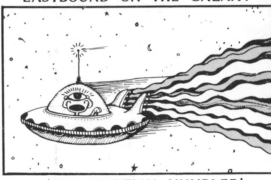

'EASTBOUND ON THE GALAXY'

'THE MARTIAN MUMBLER'

Getting a Handle

Your handle is your CB alternate personality code name. You might only get to know the folks that you meet on the CB by their handles. The best way to get one might be to have your friends think one up for you. You might go through a few, but eventually one will stick.

'That Ol' Tennessee Moonshiner'

Breaking the Channel

There are twenty-three channels for use, and each one may have as many as hundreds of users in certain areas. With so many folks using CB, you need to make sure that the channel is not in use before bulldozing your way in. The most common way to do that is to "break the channel." Always listen to see if someone is talking. Then you can say, *"Break five,"* (if you're on channel 5) and usually, if the channel is free, someone will come back and say, *"Go, breaker,"* or you might be asked to *"Stand by,"* or *"Hold on."* If you don't hear anything, you can assume that the channel is clear and make your call. Other things you might hear for breaking the channel are *"Break, break,"* *"Breakity-break,"* *"Breaker broke break,"* etc. Asking for and giving a break keeps the channels from drifting into total madness.

"Break, Channel 5. Anyone on this nickel channel?"

Radio Check

One of the first things you'll want to do with your rig is to get a "radio check." This is when you call out on the channel for the purpose of finding out how well your radio is performing. A typical radio check might go like this:

Break eleven for a radio check.

Go ahead, radio check.

10-4. You got the Big Dummy, KBD1007. Who we got there?

You got the Alligator, KAA2001. You're comin' in good here —putting about nine pounds on my meter. Got good modulation, c'mon.

10-4, good buddy. We appreciate the check. We're gonna back 'em on out. The Big Dummy, KBD1007 clear.

Folks can give you information in a radio check in two ways. They can listen to you and tell you how it sounds to them. If you are kind of weak they might say that they *"got you back in there."* A fair signal might get a *"definitely making the trip."* Strong signals can get you a *"wall-to-wall"* report, or *"you're blowin' smoke."* Another way to give a radio check is by using an S-meter (signal strength meter). Many radios have an S-meter on them. (see illustration) Stations that you talk to will move your S-meter to varying degrees, depending on the strength of their signal and their location. When that guy was saying that *"you're putting about nine pounds on my meter,"* he meant that his S-meter was reading 9 when you were talking to him. For higher readings like 20 or 40 or so, folks sometimes say, *"You're pegging my meter,"* or *"You're walking tall!"* Ways to describe how you are doing are as countless as the sands of the Ganges River.

[16]

Got you way back in there.

We got a weak copy on ya.

Definitely making the trip—
Good copy.

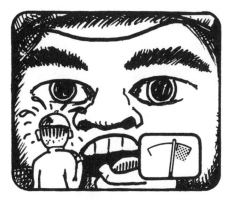

Wall to wall & tree top tall—
Bodacious.

BUSTING MY SPEAKER

PEGGING MY METER

Channels

There are 23 different channels you can use to talk on. Some channels are used for specific things, so you need to know how to do it on those channels. Some communities have an agreed-upon channel that the CBers there use. You can ask around and find out if there is one in your community.

Channel 9 may be used only for communications involving *immediate or potential emergency situations* and/or assistance to motorists. Don't use it unless you have to. Also, if you hear a *10-33* on your channel, that means emergency traffic. Try to help out. This may mean just being quiet.

Channel 11 is used throughout the country as a meeting place where you can give someone a shout and (after you connect) then move over to another channel.

Break, Channel 11!

Go, Breaker!

How about ya, Big Dummy? You on the channel?

10-4. Who I got there? Come on.

Ya got the Moonshiner here. Let's go to that one-three channel, break.

10-4. This is the Big Dummy KBD1007 and we're clear.

Channel 19 is the Trucker's channel—it's used by folks on the road to communicate about what's happening on the road. The truckers keep in touch about the traffic and highway conditions, accidents or hazards. They also use it as a sort of Yellow Pages to find out a good place to eat, directions, or where to park their rig for the night. Also, truckers use Channel 19 to keep track of Smokey the Bear. The Smokies are also on the channel, and are often aided by motorists. This makes the highways much smarter and safer.

Also, truckers use these channels:

    17—most of California
    15—around Los Angeles
    21—Southern California
    10—Canada

mmmmmm....HOWDY.

A typical Channel 19 example:

Break, one-nine, for a Southbound 18-wheeler on this I-65·

You got one—bring it on!

10-4 there, good buddy. How's it looking over your shoulder?

She's looking good. Those bridges are kind of icy back there. Other than that she's clear on back to Circle City.

10-4. Definitely appreciate the information. We got on at the Musical City, and we had a Smokey on the move about the 18 mile marker southbound there, 10-4?

10-4. We don't want to feed no bears. You have a green light to Circle City and can put the hammer down, fer sure. Y'all have a good trip today and a better trip tomorrow, and we'll catch ya on the flip. This here's the one Flyin' Wheeler. We're southbound and down!

Okay there, Flyin' Wheeler. 3's and 8's and all them good numbers on ya. You got the Music City Motormouth and we gone.

How 'boutcha, Big Dummy. Did you make it over to this one-three channel, break?

10-4. Yes, I did.

What would be yer 10-20 there, Mister Dummy?

Uhh, I'm located at the corner of Fourteenth Avenue and Laurel Drive.

Is that your home 20? Come on.

Uhh, 10-4.

Those cottonpickers were saying, *"10-4"* and *"10-20"*. They are using ten-signals, which are agreed-upon radio shorthand that folks use throughout the country. The calls go from 10-0 to 10-100. Here are some of the more common ten-signals:

10-1	Can't hear	*10-13*	Weather and road conditions
10-2	Loud and clear		
10-3	Stand by	*10-20*	Location
10-4	Yes, Okay, Roger	*10-27*	Moving to Channel - -
10-5	Relay, Repeat information for another station	*10-30*	Illegal use of radio
		10-33	Emergency traffic on the channel
10-6	Busy at present		
10-7	Out of service, Off the air	*10-34*	Request for assistance
		10-36	Correct time
10-8	In service, On the air	*10-46*	Assist motorist
10-9	Repeat	*10-77*	Negative contact
10-10	Stand by	*10-100*	Rest stop

Knobs and Dials

Let's take a gander at a new CB radio. It has all kinds of fancy knobs and dials and switches on it, and you might be wondering what they are all for. Here is a list of common ones and what they do.

RECEIVING

None of these affect how well you will get out.

Volume, Off/On—turns your set on. It adjusts the loudness of what you are listening to.

Squelch—filters out background noise, static, and weak stations. There's a threshold level, and if you turn to just past the threshold you'll cut out most of the noise but still get most of the strong stations on the channel. The further you go past that threshold, the stronger a station has to be in order for you to receive him, and you may miss out on some of the calls.

Channel Selector—selects which of the possible 23 channels you are transmitting and receiving on.

Noise Limiter and Noise Blanker (ANL & NB)—These switches cut down on static and ignition and motor noise. They help filter out noise interference to keep it from getting into your receiver and making it harder for you to hear.

Delta Tune—is a control provided on some transceivers which makes it possible for you to bring in folks who are a little off the center of a channel. Try different settings of this while listening to the station you want to hear.

RF Gain Knob—cuts down the RF (radio frequency) volume in your receiver amplifier. It can be adjusted to cut down noise on nearby stations. It has a knob which gives you lots of possible settings. Run with the RF gain up all the way unless you get close to a station and it starts sounding so loud that it distorts in your receiver. Also, you can turn this down like you would a squelch if the ratchet-jawing on the channel is bothering you.

Distant-Local—is an attenuator that in the Local position prevents local up-close CB radio traffic from overdriving your receiver. The Distant position is the normal one which gives you the full range and sensitivity of your receiver.

Meter—Most meters have two scales—one for transmitting and one for receiving. One lets you know how strong a signal you are putting out and the other lets you know how strong a signal you are picking up. The first one is a *relative power out meter*. The second is a *signal strength meter* (S-meter).

 SENDING

Push to Talk Button—is on the mike. You have to push it to transmit and let go of it to receive. You can't hear anybody if you're holding that button in!

Modulation Light—This light will vary in brightness while you are talking into the mike. Its fluctuations will let you see how your voice is getting out.

Mike Gain—increases the strength of your modulation. Ask somebody for a check to tell you at what point your signal starts to distort or break up as you are increasing the volume. That will let you know where the best place is to run that thing.

P.A.—allows you to turn your CB into a public address system. There is a jack in the back where you can plug in a cord that runs to a loudspeaker. You can even put that loudspeaker under the hood of your mobile if you want.

Skipland

On some days, you might hear people talking from far away places not within the usual range of your radio. The reason that you receive these long-distance stations is because these radio waves are bouncing off the ionosphere, layers of particles above the earth. The sun causes these layers to become electrically charged and act like a mirror. So at certain times the radio waves can be reflected back to the earth, skipping great distances with leaps and bounds. That's why we call it the "skip".

The stations you hear may be using unusual names and numbers. They are also probably using gigantic antennas and high-powered transmitters. If you try to talk back to them from your weak little mobile, they may not hear you. Don't be alarmed. Legally, you're not supposed to talk further than 150 miles anyway. It may be hard to find a clear channel during this time. Just wait a little while, and the skip will roll out just like it came in. Usually there is no skip at night.

PAYING YOUR DUES TO THE F.C.C.
GETTING A LICENSE

The use of CB radio is governed by the Federal Communications Commission. The F.C.C. issues licenses, sets standards on operation and equipment, and sometimes monitors the activities and goings-on.

To operate a CB you are required to have a license. While more than half of the radios in the country are operated without one, the F.C.C. would rather that you didn't. Currently, the F.C.C. receives 300,000–325,000 applications a month! Since it is now taking as long as three months to receive your license back, applying for one should be one of the first things you do.

This license will make you responsible for whatever happens on your rig. Not everyone in your family will need to get a license—one license will cover all of you. If you have a business, one license will cover all your employees too. Be sure to indicate on your application how many radios you will be running under this license. Be sure to add on an extra one or two units to cover any future additions.

To get a license, you need to be 18 years of age and pay a $4 fee. No exam is required. The license is good for five years and is renewable. Applications usually come with all new rigs, but if you happen to not get one or if you buy a used rig which doesn't have one, you can get an application by writing the F.C.C. Field Office nearest you and ask for F.C.C. Form 505—Application for Class D License in Citizen's Radio Service.

Send the application and filing fee to:

Federal Communications Commission
Gettysburg, PA   17325

They'll send you a copy of your license, which will contain your station identification numbers.

The F.C.C. wants to keep CB a good reliable means of communication for the greatest number of folks in local areas. They frown on skip talkers and folks running extremely high power that interferes with other people.

The F.C.C. has recently relaxed many of its rules and regulations concerning CB. For example, they no longer restrict folks from using CB as a hobby. On the other hand, they plan to enforce the regulations they still have more strictly. (They have the authority to issue warrants for illegal operation, which may result in the loss of equipment, fines, and possible jail sentences. Mercy sakes!)

The F.C.C. requires that you have a current copy of the rules. If you can't find a cheap copy at your radio equipment store, you can get a copy of the F.C.C. rules and regulations having to do with CB radio by writing the U.S. Government Printing Office, Washington, D.C. 20402. Ask for Volume VI of the F.C.C. Rules and Regulations. Include a check for $5.35, which will get you the rules and also entitle you to receive any future additions to the rules for free. Be prepared for some mind-twisting government documents!

Remember that Channel 11 is reserved as a calling channel, and Channel 9 is reserved for emergency traffic.

You are expected to use your assigned station identification number at the beginning and end of each transmission. This is not meant to interfere with your communication but if you don't use your call numbers at all you will be suspected of not having any. Handles can be used with, but not as a substitute for, call numbers.

The use of a linear amplifier (kicker) on the CB bands is not legal, and having a linear amplifier present (i.e. under your seat) is considered "de facto" evidence of its use.

Don't use obscene or profane language on the air.

You should not in any way intentionally interfere with the communications of other stations. Nor can you deliberately transmit off frequency (a feat which requires tampering with your rig).

Your communication with another station should be limited to five minutes, with a one-minute waiting period before your next call. In other words, don't hog the channel.

Never transmit the word May-Day or any other international distress signal unless there is a confirmed "grave and imminent danger to life or property."

If we remember how many fellow CBers there are, and that we're all in this together, everything will be all right! 10-4!

CHAPTER 2

Buying a New Rig

CB radios can be constructed in many different ways and come with lots of "extras". These extras, most of which are used for listening, make the difference in the price of most radios. The many combinations of these features makes for a lot of different CB radios on the market. Now it doesn't matter if you are driving a Volkswagen or a Cadillac, you can still get around. And with a moderate expense you can get into the CB action. In fact, the reason that we call these features "extras" is because they are extra and not necessary to get out well.

Legally you aren't supposed to improve your transmitting quality by boosting the power. So manufacturers try to improve the circuitry in other ways, and also add things that let you pull in weak stations or cut down on noise and interference— such as a squelch and a noise limiter. Other extras and added features do help, but are not critical. Don't get snowed into thinking you need a crystal lattice filter or phase locked loop in order to get out, because it isn't true.

"HOW'S IT LOOKIN' OVER YOUR SHOULDER ?"
"SHE'S LOOKING MIGHTY GOOD.
LET THE HAMMER DOWN."

Keep in mind you are going to need an antenna and coaxial cable. This is one of the most important factors in how your radio is going to work.

The power that your radio will put out affects its performance and its price. The power used by a CB is expressed in two ways: as power input and power output. The power input is the amount of power used by the transmitter to produce what goes out. The power output is the amount of power which actually gets out of the radio. Power is measured in watts. The FCC has set a limit of 5 watts in and 4 watts out, which is what most new rigs deliver. So that's the best you can legally do. The amount of power you put out affects your range of communication. Four watts can provide relatively good communication in a radius of 10 to 20 miles or more. Limiting communications to 4 watts was designed to improve the quality of local CB communication by cutting down interference from the traffic of neighboring communities. It also allows there to be many folks on the air at once.

Now maybe you aren't too concerned about getting out the maximum distance possible. There are cheaper rigs with fewer watts. The most common kind is the walkie-talkie which can put out one or more watts. Walkie-talkies' lower power combined with the lower antenna size and height keep them from getting out as well as other rigs. A stronger rig will help talk around them hills and buildings, and will cut through the interference better, so it never hurts to have more watts. Usually it's worth the added expense to have the most power out that you can get.

Making Something out of the Advertising

Now suppose you are interested in getting a CB radio but don't know much about them. You could be strolling through the neighborhood shopping center and be surprised by a big display of CBs. You try to stretch your imagination and comprehend all the advertising boasting of the quality of their inner workings, but it leaves you at a loss. Well, don't let that bog you down. Here are some common features you may run into:

How many channels?

You'll find folks on every channel to meet and ratchet jaw with so you'll probably want as many channels as you can get. The more channels you got the better chance you have of finding a clear one. Having more channels doesn't help you get out any better—it merely gives you more spaces for talking to folks. You can also find rigs that come with one or two channels and have places where you can add channels by inserting more crystals, if you want to. A set of crystals for transmit and receive will cost around $5. These rigs work fine for communication out on the road or with your home base and can have channel 9 for emergencies. Most of them come with maximum legal power and work as well as some 23 channel rigs.

Only radios marked **FCC Type Accepted** will be legal to use after November, 1978. Definitely a consideration when buying a new one.

A *Power Mike* is a microphone with a built-in amplifier. It is usually sold as a separate item. Most new radios have ample modulation with the microphones that they come with, but a power mike can help out most any rig. They don't increase your power above what your radio is rated, but they make your voice sound louder and generally carry further. Power mikes increase your modulation somewhat.

SSB? ? ? ?
(LSB and USB—Lower and Upper Sideband)

Some more expensive rigs use SSB (single sideband). Single sideband is a method used to put all the power being transmitted into a more compact signal. Also it's legal to run up to 12 watts using SSB. A SSB signal has 1½ to 2 times the range of an AM signal. But you can only talk to other stations having SSB radio. SSB only takes half the space that a regular AM signal takes. So you get two SSB channels for every AM channel. This does not mean that you won't get interfered with by the other AM stations using the same channel. On your regular AM rig, SSB stations will sound muffled and garbled. Sideband is becoming increasingly popular, although almost everyone still uses regular AM.

Tubes or transistors— Transistors are best for mobiles because of convenient DC battery power available. Their ruggedness in the face of vibrations and the bump and grind of mobile traveling gives longer lasting performance than a tube radio would. However, a tube radio makes for a good base station. They run off 110 volts AC and can take certain kinds of electrical punishment (such as a high SWR or a direct antenna short) that would leave a transistor radio French-fried.

Dual Conversion IF— A little fancier receive circuit that gives some added clarity of reception over single conversion.

Filters— ceramic, crystal lattice, and mechanical; these are different ways of filtering your receiver in order to prevent *bleeding over* of conversations on channels next to the one that you are using.

Automatic modulation gain circuit (and limiter)— this gizmo maintains a high level of modulation over a wide range of voice inputs. It also prevents over-modulation.

Specifications—These are usually talked about with a lot of fancy figures thrown in that add to the confusion. When buying a new rig, you should try to get the best ratings you can.

New 23-channel FCC Type Accepted rigs have ample selectivity for most applications and have equally good sensitivity. *Selectivity* is the receiver's ability to differentiate between an adjacent channel signal and the desired one, so folks aren't bleeding over on your channel. *Adjacent Channel Rejection* also has to do with this. *Sensitivity* is a measurement of how well your radio can hear. The more sensitive the radio, the weaker the signal that the receiver can pick up. Good sensitivity can really make the difference for a base station and give you a longer range of reception. For mobile stations it is less critical since the ignition and static noise of the vehicle will sometimes drown out the weak stations that would have been picked up by a sensitive radio.

Here's a typical set of specs for a good quality rig and what they mean.

THUNDERBOLT 3000 SPECIFICATIONS

Sensitivity— 0.5 μV for 10 dB S+N/N; **Selectivity**— 6 kHz at -6 dB; **Adjacent Channel Rejection**— - 50 dB at ± 10 kHz; **Audio Power Output**—2 watts at 10% THD; **Modulation**—90% typical; **Spurious Output**— -50 dB max; **RF Power Output**— 4 watts.

Sensitivity—0.5 μV for 10 dB S+N/N

Sensitivity gives you an idea of how good it is at pulling out a weak signal.

The Sensitivity figure "μV" means microvolts—the lower the number, the better.

The conditions. It's the "signal plus noise-to-noise ratio" The larger the number of dBs, the better.

Selectivity—6 kHz at -6 dB

These two are related and they have to do with how clear your channel is gonna sound if someone is using the channel next to yours.

A lower figure here is better. They're usually between 5 and 6.

The usual conditions.

Adjacent Channel Rejection— -50 dB at ± 10 kHz

Some manufacturers don't give selectivity the way it is here. They use the term Selectivity instead of Adjacent Channel Rejection.

A larger figure here is better, like -75 dB.

The usual conditions.

Audio Power Output— 2 watts at 10% THD

It's a little amplifier just like a stereo and this is how much power it has to drive the speaker.

The more watts, the louder it can sound at full volume. 2 or 3 watts is plenty.

This is the usual CB standard for clean sound. THD means Total Harmonic Distortion.

Modulation— 90% typical

This is how much of the available power the transmitter actually uses.

100% is ideal, but they can't cut it that close on an assembly line.

Spurious Output— -50 dB max

This is the kind of garble that makes a mess on other channels, TV as well as CB. It's usually not mentioned.

This is the FCC minimum. The larger this figure the better.

RF Power Output—4 watts

The basic power of your transmitter.

This is the FCC maximum. It's roughly the same as 5 watts *input.*

[33]

Power requirements— If you are getting a radio for your car, get one with 12—13.8 volts DC rating. For a base station you can get a radio that runs off of 110 volts AC. Some companies make a radio that has both kinds of power supplies for using a radio as both a mobile and as a base station. *Positive or Negative ground* means it can be hooked up easily to either a positive or negative ground vehicle.

Mobile or Base???

You can use a mobile radio as a base station by using a 12-volt DC converter that plugs in the wall. A converter (power supply) costs about $15—25. This will work just about as well as a more expensive base station radio would.

Now that you got past all that, of course you will want to try some of those fancy beauties on for size. Ask your dealer if you can try one. Grab that old microphone and ask some local CBer how you're getting out.

"How about a radio check for 250 bucks? C'mon."

Buying a Used Rig

There are many used radios available, especially those that only have a few channels, as many folks are getting newer all-channel rigs. Many of these older CBs are of fine quality, but just don't have the compactness and extras that some of the new ones do. That's all right. Here is a way to get a good rig for a good price. You should see if it operates on transmit and receive. Check and see if that used radio has the channels that you want, too. Some older rigs have crystals that are hard to find and you have to send away for them, so make sure you are getting the channels you want, or that crystals for the rig are easily available.

Some rigs have tuneable receiving which lets you tune in the different CB channels like you would tune in the stations on your AM car radio. If your CB has this you won't need receiving crystals.

Some tube rigs may not have 100% modulation or full legal power and may need some pepping up or a power mike. You can have it tuned up by a qualified radio man.

So how 'boutcha, Big Dummy, you still on the channel?

Yeah, I got my ears on. I just managed to make it through these pages, mercy sakes!

10-4 there. You getting familiar with that there hunk of junk?

Roger D, good buddy. I've just been modulating on my buddy's rig here, and I think I'll go out and get myself one of these here squawk boxes.

10-Roger there, Big Dummy. We'll pick you up on 11 in a short short. We'll back 'em on out of here and catch you later.

CHAPTER THREE

Mobiles

CB has gotten as big as it has because of its great possibilities for communication while you're rolling down the road. It's great for talking back to your Home 20 and finding out how it's going back there, as well as getting connected with the flow of things out on the Interstate or local highways. Since most folks are going to want to start out with a rig in their four wheeler, we'll get right into how to install one in your car and mount a good antenna on it, too.

Installing Your CB

There are several good things to remember when you are going to put a new rig in your mobile. The first thing that comes to mind is where to mount it. Often it is a matter of the driver's druthers as to where the radio is mounted. There are some practical things, though, to keep in mind. You'll want it within easy reach and be clearly visible when you're driving. You don't want to end up in the ditch because you had to dive for a mike to answer some local feller. It should be out of the way of the gear shift or emergency brake. Make sure the mike cord and other wires won't get tangled in the steering wheel or the gas and brake pedals, and that it is in a place where it won't get kicked or sat on. Also, heat can damage a rig, so don't mount it right under your car heater. So it usually turns out that the rig is mounted somewhere under the dash close to the driver, or occasionally on the ceiling close to the driver.

10-4 ON THAT TELEPHONE POLE, I'LL BE 10-7 FOR A SHORT SHORT...

DON'T FORGET YOU'RE DRIVING

Once you have figured out where you'd like to mount it, drill the holes for the mount, being careful not to hit anything behind the dashboard, and screw that bracket up there and bolt the CB onto it. Now is a good time to figure out how this rig is going to get its electricity. Most radios have two wires coming out of the back for the power: they are red and black. Usually, red is positive and black is negative. Most radios with two wires like this can be used for either positive- or negative-ground vehicles. (Check instructions with radio to see if this is the case.)

It's important to check to see whether your vehicle is positive or negative ground. Just lift the hood and check to see which battery terminal is attached to the frame of the vehicle. Most cars are negative ground (the frame being ground) but *make sure first!!* Hooking your CB up the wrong way can damage it—set the ole set a-smoking.

Negative Ground Installation

Run an insulated wire of the kind you can get at automobile parts stores for car wiring systems. Run it directly from the positive lead of the CB to the positive terminal of the car battery. Put an in-line fuse in this wire close to the battery to protect your car electrical system. Make sure you tape all connections with good quality electrical tape. The negative wire can be bolted to the metal body of the car somewhere, because the negative terminal of the battery is also fastened to the metal. This grounding will supply the negative connection to your radio.

The other way to do it is to tap into the car fuse panel (see picture).

This makes it so you only have to run a wire from the fuse panel to the radio, a shorter distance than all the way to the battery.

It's a good idea to have a separate fuse for your CB. Most CBs come with a fuse in their power supply lead. Never use anything bigger than a 3-amp fuse for a transistorized radio. Having a fuse can possibly save you some future repair bills by offering added protection.

Positive Ground Installation

Many trucks and semis are *positive-ground*. For this, you have to do another kind of thing in hooking up your radio.

If you haven't got a rig yet, definitely check and see whether your vehicle is positive or negative ground. If it is positive ground, get a rig that can operate either way and it will save you a lot of trouble. Check the owner's manual to determine if your radio can be operated either positive or negative ground.

Most radios have two small wires, one red and one black. In this case, just hook the red wire to some bolt or screw on the body of the vehicle. Hook the black wire through an in-line fuse holder to the negative terminal of the battery, or to a hot terminal in the fuse box.

Some radios just have one small wire coming out of the back. This is the hot lead. It is usually positive. The case of the radio provides the ground connection. Some radios have a switch or can be rewired inside for positive ground. Always make sure to use the proper fuse if you have to experiment.

If you have a vehicle with only 6 volt DC, there are 6 to 12 volt converters that you can buy in order to feed your rig the right menu.

Mercy sakes! Don't turn on your rig without an antenna made especially for CB connected to it. No other antenna will do; not the AM radio one; no, not your TV antenna either; nope, only the real thing.

Don't ever try to bypass your radio's fuse, either.

HOW 'BOUT
YA SOUTH
DAKOTA? YOU
GOT ONE MOOSE
TRYING FOR YA...

Mobile Antennas

The heart of CB communications is mobile-to-mobile and mobile-to-base operations. The ears you have on your mobile definitely play an important part in how you get out.

There are many different kinds of mounts and places you can put your antenna. You could stick that ear just about any place on your mobile, but some places have advantages over others.

The metal body of your vehicle is actually a part of your antenna. Where you place the antenna in relation to the car body will affect the radiation pattern of your signal, which will be the strongest across the longest portion of the vehicle.

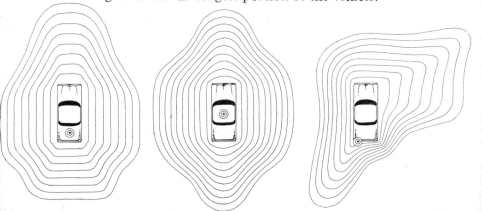

Whips

The best physical length for a CB antenna which would still
be practical for mobile use would be 102-108 inches, depending
on if it includes an impact spring or not. Impact or recoiled
springs bend when struck and absorb shock. Although we've
seen these nine-foot whips on the tops of some vehicles, they
tend to mix it with the tree limbs and garage roofs, etc. So you
see a lot of nine-foot whips mounted on back bumpers.
This takes advantage of getting out better with a full-length
whip. A bumper mount has other disadvantages. It puts the
antenna lower to the ground where its radiation can be blocked
by nearby obstructions. The nine-foot whip, when mounted on
the back bumper, works best in the direction towards the front
of the car.

Loading Coils

Antennas with loading coils make the antenna physically shorter while maintaining the correct "electrical length." These are not quite as effecient as a nine-foot whip, but have the advantage of being shorter, so they can be mounted higher on the vehicle. Antennas less then 3½ feet long are not recommended, except in portable or temporary situations, or where nothing else can be used. The efficiency of the small antenna can be increased by using two on either side of a vehicle. In short antennas, the coil replaces a large chunk of the  9-foot antenna. Since much of the RF energy is concentrated in the coil, you will want it up as high as possible. We recommend center or top loaded antennas over bottom loaded. Bottom loaded antennas work well only when mounted on the roof or some place clear of other metal objects.

Metal vs. Fiberglass

Fiberglass antennas usually come in two main lengths—the nine foot and the four foot whip. The shorter ones have a loading coil embedded in the fiberglass. If bought from a reputable manufacturer, they will give many years of service, even under rough use. A spring is recommended on the 9 foot model. These antennas usually come factory adjusted for resonance. They should not be tampered with.

Metal antennas come in every length and design imaginable. They have the advantage of being slightly less conspicuous. Quality varies greatly according to what materials are used. Aluminum antennas are not recommended. You should use a base spring on the nine foot steel whips. Usually the kind with the coil in the base is best for roof mount and the kind with the coil in the center or the top is best for trunk mount. Most coil loaded antennas have a means for adjusting the length, which is a good thing to have.

Twin Antennas

Twins are very popular on big trucks, campers, and other vehicles where it is not possible to mount a single antenna on the roof. Two identical antennas are used with a special set of coaxial cables called a *co-phase harness*. This is nothing more than two equal lengths of coax usually 11'9" long, both hooked to the same connector.

The two antennas work together to produce a stronger signal in two directions. If the antennas are at least 8 feet apart, such as on the two mirrors of a big truck, they will get out best forwards and backwards. If they are less than 8 feet apart, they will get out best sideways. This, in effect, gives you a mobile beam antenna.

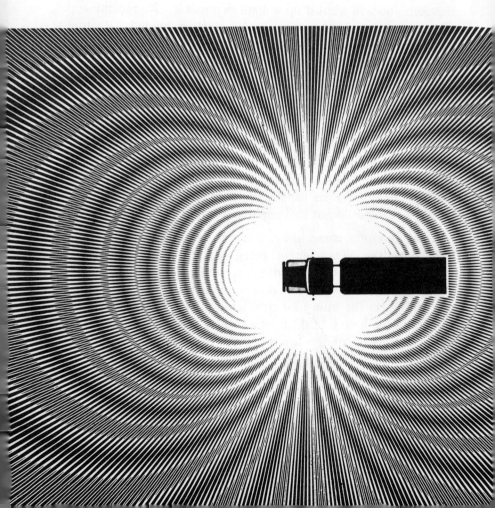

Mounts

The best place to mount a single antenna is smack dab in the center of the roof. This is the highest place you can put it. This gets it up and out of the way of obstacles that could interfere with the radio waves coming off the antenna. The metal frame of the car is used as part of the antenna. Mounting the antenna in the center gives a balanced and uniform radiation pattern which will allow you to get out well in all directions.

We can give you some tips on mounting that ear on your roof. First off you will have to drill a small hole in the roof. Now don't cringe, for heaven's sakes, it ain't that bad! There are a couple of things you can do to the hole when it comes time to sell your car. There are small rubber plugs that you can buy that will seal your roof right up. Or there are patch kits that come with matching spray paint that will make her just like new. You could even leave your antenna right on the old car and actually enhance the resale value of that old bucket of bolts you have been driving! One final piece of advice is needed here when talking about roof mounts: make sure that you have a good sealing rubber grommet on that antenna connection to your roof to keep the rain out.

A convenient way to find a place for drilling a hole is by temporarily removing your dome light. It is usually attached with screws near the center of the roof. From this vantage point, you can check out your roof and see how easy it will be to mount it there. It may be possible to snake your coax above the roof liner to the front of the car. Here you can remove the corner molding next to the windshield and bring the coax down to the dash.

When you climb up on the roof, be sure to distribute your weight well and not put any dents in it. Your roof is only 1/8" thick so use a short drill bit or shim up your drill bit with a block of wood so you don't run through into the headliner. Use a nail or punch to start your hole; otherwise your bit may skate around on the roof making scratchmarks and other scrapings and designs.

DRIP

DRIP

There are ways of mounting that don't get you into punching holes in your roof or fenders. There are gutter mount antennas that attach to the car's rain gutter; there are trunk lip antennas that fasten to the trunk lip. There are mirror mounts for truck type mirrors. These can be used on metal package racks on top of station wagons too. There's even magnetic mounts that magnetically hold the antenna down on the metal roof. For these you do have to run the coax through the window. But they're real easy to transfer from one vehicle to another. A magnetic mount will withstand winds up to 100 miles per hour. Ball mounts conform to the curves in the vehicle. Be sure the center hole you put in the body is large enough, so the mounting nut won't touch metal. . . .And there's always the good old vise grips for a temporary mount.

Hooking Up The Coax

O.K. We got the radio all wired up. Now we got to hook up that radio to some ears. In order for the radio signal to get from the CB to an antenna, you need some kind of wire to connect the two together. Usually a special kind of two-conductor wire is used, called coax (*Koh*-axe, from coaxial). This special wire is made up of an inner wire covered with a plastic sheath, and an outer wire mesh lead that in turn is covered by a black outer covering. Now there are several types of coax, but only two kinds are much good for CB—RG 58/U and RG 8/U coax. Unless you're running 1000 watts in your mobile, RG 58/U will work fine. RG 59/U is sometimes used for phasing harnesses.

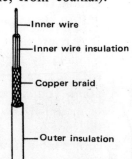

Inner wire
Inner wire insulation
Copper braid
Outer insulation

It's good when installing a CB to get the coax up and out of the way, not only just for looks, but also to keep it from getting stepped on or tripped over. You can hide it under the floor mats, under the door mud guards, wall panels, window posts, or roof headliner. Avoid flattening or crimping or wearing the insulation off.

Coax Connectors

The coax will need to be connected to the back of the radio and to the antenna. This is done with a connector (such as a PL 259) that attaches to the coax.

The coax and connector are often supplied when you buy an antenna. Sometimes, though, you may need to attach your own connector, especially if you make your own antenna. We talk about attaching connectors to coax later in the book.

Connecting the Coax to the Antenna

Some antennas have the coax already attached. Other antennas either have a connector that plugs into the base of the antenna or two terminals which attach to the antenna mount. There are a few other ways to do this, so check the instructions that come with your antenna.

It is important that the shield of the coax be securely connected to the body of the vehicle. The shield is the larger outside braided wire on the coaxial cable. Usually, the mount of the antenna provides this connection. If you are using a mirror mount type, make sure that your mirror braces are making good connection with the body of the truck.

Sometimes if the connection is not made properly, the antenna will not work right. Although you may be able to receive somewhat, you may not get out very well. Sometimes scraping down to bare metal is necessary in order to make a good connection.

YEAH, 10-4. I'VE DEFINITELY GOT AN EAR PROBLEM, 10-4!

SWR

Is Your Antenna Working Right?

The length of your antenna makes a difference because the radio waves have a certain length. You must match your antenna's length to that of the radio wave. When your antenna is the wrong length, some of this power does not radiate, but is bounced back into the coax, and into the radio itself. If this *reflected* power is too high, it can cause your power transistors some problems. Besides, it's a waste of energy that could get out there and do its thing for you. So you want the least amount of reflected power and the most amount of forward power as possible.

You can find out if your antenna is the right length by using an SWR meter. An SWR meter can be purchased at most radio stores or borrowed from a local CBer.

SWR means Standing Wave Ratio. Sounds high falootin', don't it? Well, don't let it scare you off. It's simple.

Checking SWR

You need a short, 1-2 foot long coaxial cable with a connector on each end. Plug in one end to your rig and the other to the socket on the meter labeled TXMTR or TX. Plug the coax that goes to your antenna into the socket on your meter labeled to ANT.

Turn the knob on the meter all the way down. Put the switch in the FORWARD position. Turn on your radio and listen for other stations. It should be working normally. Tune your channel selector to some unused channel where you won't bother anyone.

Press your mike button and without saying anything into the microphone, adjust the knob on the SWR meter until the meter reads SET. or full scale. Then flip the switch to REFLECTED and read the SWR scale of your meter.

Now that you know what it is, take your finger off that button! If the meter reads less than 1.5, your antenna is working properly. If it reads more than 2, your antenna probably needs adjustment. If it reads more than 3, check all connections at the antenna for possible bad connections; or the antenna or the center wire of the coax might be touching the body of the vehicle.

Adjusting your Antenna

So let's say that your SWR turns out to be 2:1, and you want to bring it down. There are two ways to change an antenna's SWR: one is to lengthen it, and the other is to shorten it. You can figure out which way to go in the following manner: Take an SWR reading on channel 1, then take one on channel 23. Which channel had the higher SWR? If the SWR was higher on channel 23, you need to shorten the tip. If the SWR was higher on channel 1, you need to lengthen the tip. Move it about ¼" at a time.

Most antennas have a set screw you can loosen so that the tip can slide up and down. If this does not give enough adjustment, you can clip or file ¼" at a time off the bottom of the tip and re-insert it in the coil. Make sure to reset the SWR meter every time you take a reading.

One good rule to remember when adjusting antennas is, if you bring your hand near the loading coil or top of the antenna and the SWR goes down, the tip of the antenna needs to be

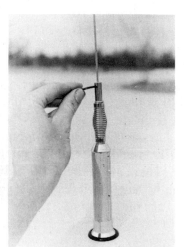

lengthened; if the SWR goes up, the tip needs shortening. If you're using twins, make equal adjustments to each side at the same time.

Don't cut too much off now!

If the SWR is high and you are using a transistorized rig to check it, do not hold the mike button in for more than ten seconds at a time. This is to protect the power transistors.

CHAPTER 4

Base Stations

Once you've been hooked on a CB in your mobile, you'll be wanting one at home, too, for that late night ratchet-jawing on the channel. You'll find base stations with a whole bee hive of activity surrounding them, keeping the folks in a community informed of who's where and what's happening. You'll find the same true along the highways where CB-equipped truck stops will keep folks in touch for long stretches, taking messages and relaying information for the truckers and travelers and folks that get to know each other on the super-slab.

How about ya, you seen that Pony Express today? Ya got the Road Runner here.

10-4. Howdy, Road Runner. He was by a short while ago and said he would meet you in Windy City. He might still have a copy on us. You want me to give him a shout?

10-4. Let him know we're putting the pedal to the metal and doing it to it for sure. Gonna try to bring it on up there. Come on.

10-4!

Installing a Base Station

A base station is a little different from the mobile. It's usually bigger, and it runs on 120 volts AC, so you can plug it right into the wall. You can set it up on a desk or bookshelf— somewhere that you find easily accessible and easy to monitor. Installing it is no problem: plug it in and hook up an antenna and coax, and you're in business. There are many optional base station features, but the best one to have behind you is a good solid antenna that will put it out for you.

Using a Solid State Mobile Rig as a Base

Most base station rigs just plug right into the wall. If you plan to use a mobile rig for a base station, you will need to hook up a converter or use a car battery and battery charger.

Since most mobile rigs are rather small and light weight, we suggest that you mount the rig on a shelf or on some sort of base such as wood to hold it down. If you plan to use a DC converter, make sure you get one with at least a 3 amp. capacity at 12-14 volts DC.

The DC power supply is usually a small box that plugs into an AC outlet and has 2 terminals where you can screw on the power leads to the radio. To hook up your radio, connect the red lead from the transceiver to the plus (+) terminal and the black lead to the negative (-) terminal. If your radio has no black lead, use a piece of insulated automotive type wire to connect from a screw on the radio's case to the negative terminal of the DC converter. Make sure there is a 3-amp or smaller fuse in one of these wires.

If you plan to use a car battery instead of a DC converter, you should get something to keep it in. Battery acid can and will eat your clothes and lots of other things, including your rug. There are plastic cases sold for use with electric boat motors, available at hardware stores. Using a car battery has its advantages. If you should have an AC power outage, your base will continue to function on battery power automatically. A transistorized CB transceiver will run about a week or two under normal use on a fully charged car battery.

Hooking up the car battery and charger: It should be located within fifteen feet or so from the radio, so you don't lose too much juice running long wires.

You need:
—12 volt car battery and case.
— ½ amp trickle charger (auto parts or dept. store)
— two insulated wires of different colors (each long enough to reach from the battery to the radio)
— electrical tape
— one positive battery clamp with wing nut
   one negative battery clamp with wing nut
— an in-line fuse holder with fuse (3 amps)

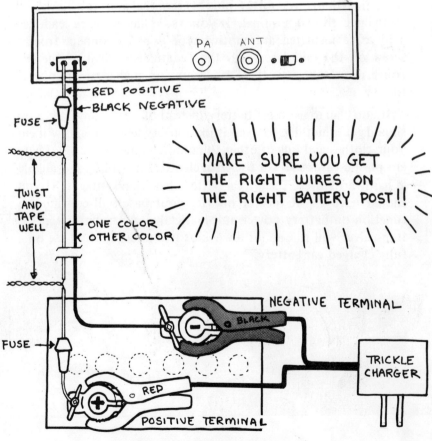

Car battery operated base station

Home 20 Antennas

Getting yourself a good set of ears is an important venture in making the trip. You can go and buy commercially-made antennas that will do a good job for you. Also, you can make your own and put it up yourself—so we include some antenna building ideas that can save you some money and also be fun to do.

When antennas get talked about, they are called by their wavelength—like a 1/4 wavelength or a 5/8 wavelength. Wavelength is the length in space of a radio wave. Your antenna is made a multiple or sub-multiple of that length, because that is the right size package for catching that particular radio wave. What we do with the CB antenna is to create the right size package for transmitting and receiving those waves.

Driving around these days you can notice a lot of different base antennas—all kinds, shapes, and sizes. The folks that modulate them talk about how well their ears do, and you might wonder what kind of difference one could have over another as far as getting out goes. Obviously, you're bound to get out better the higher you go, so stick it on up there.

That's right, folks! With a little hot coax in the a.m., Gain perks you up and gets you out!

Another thing you hear folks talk about is *gain*.

The simplest antenna, a regular ¼ wave vertical, has no gain. Other antennas are measured in how many times better than this they are. Let's say that you just bought a new antenna that has a gain of 3 dbs (db stands for decibels, which is what gain is measured in). When you hook up your four-watt rig to it, you'll increase your effective power past what your ¼ wave vertical antenna could put out by itself. A 3 db gain is approximately a doubling of power. Here's a chart that has the gain all worked out for you.

db Gain	Multiply Power by
0	1.0
1	1.2
2	1.6
3	2.0
4	2.5
5	3.0
6	4.0
7	5.0
8	6.3
9	8.0
10	10.0
11	12.6
12	15.8
13	20.0
14	25.1
15	31.6
16	40.0
17	50.2
18	63.2
19	80.0
20	100.4

If that new antenna has a gain of 6 db. and you ran 4 watts output, it would have the power equivalent of running 16 watts into a ¼ wave antenna.

One of the best ears you can get for a base rig has a gain of 16 db. From a 4 watt station, that would give an equivalent power out of 160 watts in the direction the antenna's pointed. A change of one decibel in power is a just noticeable change in loudness. It takes about 6 db. to move an S-meter one unit. In other words, if you are using a regular quarter-wave vertical antenna and switch to a beam that has 6 db. gain, the signal you transmit and receive will be stronger by one notch on yours and the other station's S-meter.

The gain we're talking about actually has to come from somewhere. In an *omnidirectional* antenna (works well in all directions), gain comes from building the antenna in such a way that the RF energy is spread out closer and flatter to the ground. This puts more of your power into radio waves that travel along the ground. It does this by taking power away from the higher angles. Most local communication is done on the ground wave. Some types of omnidirectional antennas are called *ground planes.*

The other kind of antenna that's *directional* is the *beam*, which focuses the RF energy in a narrow beam, by the use of several antenna elements. This gain is produced at the expense of RF energy that could have gone in other directions.

When buying a base antenna, don't be fooled by any fancy names or features. Judge your antenna by its stated *gain* first. Other features to look for are light weight, rugged construction, and ease of assembly. Whether you are buying an antenna or building one yourself, your first decision must be whether you want to put up a directional beam antenna or an omnidirectional vertical antenna. An omnidirectional antenna could give equal coverage for all directions locally, while a beam antenna would give you a longer range, but only in one direction at a time. You can get a TV rotator to put on that beam antenna so you can point it in whatever direction you want. Or you might possibly want both a beam and a vertical antenna for using at different times.

The FCC makes a distinction between legal heights of beams and omnidirectionals:

They say that directional antennas should be installed so that no part of the antenna exceeds 20 feet above the ground, building or tree on which it is mounted. Omnidirectional antennas should not exceed 60 feet, and may have to be lower if you are near an airport. You can check with your airport.

¼ Wave Vertical Ground Plane Antennas

The most basic CB antenna is the ¼ wave length vertical ground plane. A quarter wave ground plane has a 1 db gain above an isotropic source, which is an imaginary antenna used for electrical gain measurements. It gets out fairly well in all directions. It's the base station's equivalent of a nine-foot mobile whip.

This antenna consists of a driven element and three or four radials that act as a ground plane. The driven element receives the transmit energy from the rig, while the radials act as a ground. A ¼ wave vertical can be mounted very easily, and takes up very little room. It can be mounted on a lightweight metal pole or pipe such as is used for a TV antenna, or right on your roof or chimney. You can get an inexpensive "push-up" type pole, up to 50 feet tall, that a couple of folks can put up easily.

There are other ¼ wave length antennas that are not ground planes. They usually work about the same as a ground plane. A co-linear antenna means it is an antenna which is larger than ¼ wave.

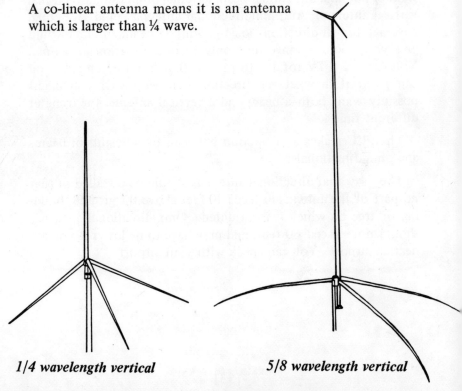

1/4 wavelength vertical   5/8 wavelength vertical

The 5/8 Wavelength Vertical Antenna

The 5/8 wavelength vertical is similar to the 1/4 wavelength vertical antenna. It too has a radiating element and three or four radials. However, the 5/8 wavelength's driven element is much longer. This is because 5/8 of a wavelength is much longer than 1/4 of a wavelength. This extra length has an effect on how the radio energy is focused. This is what gain is all about—it is not an amplification, but putting to good use all the energy that is there. The main thing about a 5/8 wavelength antenna is that it focuses its power low to the ground. A 5/8 wavelength antenna will usually have a 3 to 4.5 db gain over a 1/4 wavelength antenna. This can increase your range as much as ten miles or more, and takes advantage of the energy that otherwise would be going up, where it is useless for local communication or skip.

There are other types of omnidirectional antennas that will work similar to the 5/8 or 1/4 wavelength antenna. The best comparison in this case is by the actual gain.

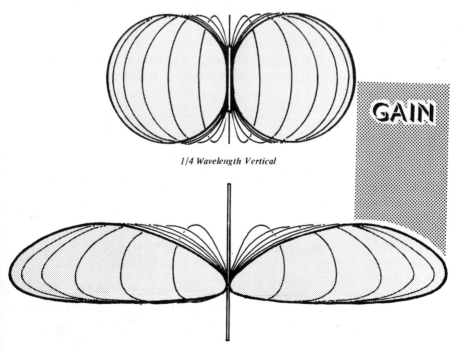

GAIN

1/4 Wavelength Vertical

5/8 Wavelength Vertical

RADIATION PATTERNS

Beams

Directional antennas, or beams, are made up of elements. An element is a length of tubing or wire positioned in such a way as to make radio waves travel in a certain direction. Usually, the more elements an antenna has, the more gain it has, and the better it will cut out interference from unwanted directions.

There are three types of elements. The *driven element* is hooked directly to your coax cable and is the one that radiates the power from your transmitter. The *reflector element* is usually slightly longer than the driven element and is positioned 4 feet or more behind the driven element. It acts like a mirror behind the driven element to reflect waves in the direction the antenna is pointing. On the other side of the driven element is the *director*, which is usually slightly shorter than the driven element. It acts like a lens to intensify the energy in the direction the antenna is pointed.

Polarization

Depending on the position of the elements, radio waves travel with either vertical (elements straight up and down) or horizontal (lying flat) polarization. All CB mobile antennas are vertically polarized.

A horizontally polarized antenna does not pick up a vertical antenna's signal as well as a vertical one would. But for communicating between two base stations it is sometimes useful to use horizontal polarization, because there will be less interference with mobiles. In this case, both stations need to be using horizontally polarized antennas.

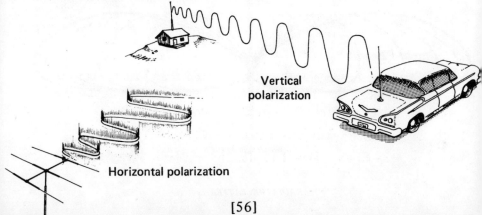

Vertical polarization

Horizontal polarization

Vertical Beams

These are the most common type of CB beam. They work well for both local and longer distance communication. They are usually made of lightweight aluminum tubing and need to have a rotator (a motor to turn the beam). Some of these beams are small enough to be turned by a TV rotator.

There are also vertical beams that change direction with the flip of a switch. Sometimes this kind of antenna is called a *scanner* or *phased verticals*. It also lets you switch from being an omnidirectional to being a beam antenna. When putting up a beam, try to keep it as far from other metal objects and antennas as possible. They could interfere with the beam's operation. Usually the vertical elements are about 18' long and are supported by a larger-diameter aluminum pipe called a *boom*. Usually the longer the boom, the higher the gain.

Typical gains for beams:

3 element — 8 db.
4 element — 11 db.
5 element — 14 db.

Stacked Beams

Stacking beams gives you more gain than just having one. Keep in mind that you will need a sturdy tower to hold one of these babies up, and a heavy-duty rotator to move it.

Approximate gains of stacked beams:

3+3—12 db. 4+4—14.5 db. 5+5—17 db. Mercy sakes!

Switchable Horizontal/Vertical Beams

These antennas combine two identical beam antennas on the same boom—one horizontal and one vertical. Each one has its own coax, with a switch to change from one to the other. Remember that on this kind of antenna the horizontal beam is not used at the same time as the vertical.

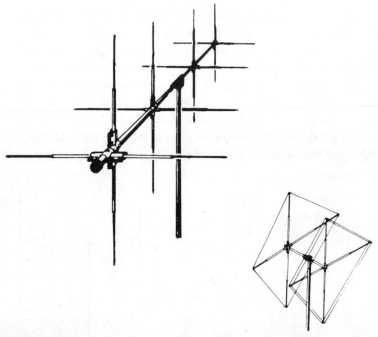

Quads

Usually, a quad has more gain per element than a regular beam. Quads use loop or square elements, usually made of wire and supported on an X-shaped frame. They also need a tower and a rotator. Some are available with switchable polarization and have two driven elements.

Depending on the number of elements and the spacing, the following gains are possible:

2 element: 9 db; 3 element: 11.5 db; 4 element; 14 db; 5 element: 17 db

Quads also can be stacked for more gain. Because of their large *capture area,* they are one of the best beams around.

Coax

When connecting your rig to an antenna, you need some kind of line to connect the two together. Now I remember once going over to one cotton picker's 10-20 and finding that he had his antenna hooked up by using 2-lead speaker wire that ran 30 feet outside to an antenna mounted on a broom handle. Mercy sakes! He was wondering how come he wasn't getting out. The best thing to use hooking up your rig is coax. Coax shields your line so that only your antenna radiates, for sure. Use RG-58 or RG-8 for right impedance match. Almost all CB antennas are made to use this kind of coax.

"10-4. I just shortened my coax. How'm I getting out? C'mon."

Also, it's best to make your coaxial line to your antenna as short as possible. That prevents resistance losses eating away at your power out. It starts to get critical when you run 100 feet or more coax. You should switch to RG-8 for that long a distance, because its losses will be much less.

RG-8 coax has larger wire, which has less resistance to electrical flow than RG-58. It is also more expensive. If you use 50 feet of RG-58 cable to run your 4 watts, about 80% of the power reaches the antenna; with RG-8, 90% reaches it. If you run 100 feet of coax, RG-58 gives you about 65% of the power to the antenna, and RG-8 is about 80%.

The letter A after the number of the coax (ex., RG-8 A/U) means that it is a new type wire that doesn't deteriorate after years of use. This is the best kind of coax to use.

There are also other numbers for coax. RG 213 A/U is the same as RG-8 A/U. Other numbers can be looked up in cable manufacturers guides.

Lightning Arrestors

Hanging that big old antenna out there is sure attractive to lightning, and your coax will bring it right on into your house, which may produce a variety of unwanted consequences, such as a light show and Roman candle effect from your rig, and the possibility of getting zapped! There are a couple of preventive measures you can take. The best thing to do during a lightning storm is to disconnect your coax from your rig and put it somewhere away from people, kids, your rig, etc. Maybe even throw it out the window!

Another thing you can do is buy an in-line lightning arrestor. It is called "in-line" because it connects right into your coaxial line. From this you run a thick copper wire to a ground rod. A ground rod is a metal rod about 6 feet long, driven into the ground. Your cold water pipes may work as well, if you haven't got a place to drive a ground rod. The thick wire connecting the arrestor to the ground rod should be run in as straight a line as possible, away from other objects, with no sharp bends in it. Also, if your antenna is mounted on a metal tower which is not in the ground, you should connect it with a thick wire to a ground rod, driven into the ground at the base of the tower. Ground rods and clamps can be purchased at any electrical supply store.

Coax splices

It's best to have your coax be one long, unbroken run from your rig to the antenna. If splices have to be made in the line, you'll want to make sure there is good electrical contact made. Use two male PL 259 coax connectors and a double female connector. Cover the complete assembly with black electrical tape to protect it from moisture.

Cutting your coax

It is a common myth that chopping off sections of your coax will help out your SWR. While it may change your SWR reading slightly, it won't necessarily help you get out any better. The best thing is to just use the shortest length of coax possible.

If the SWR is high, check all the connections in the line and make sure the antenna is the right length and has been assembled properly. Try wiggling the coax at the connector while checking the SWR to see if there is a loose connection or short where it was soldered.

Towers and Masts

The easiest method is to stick it up on the roof or attach it to the side of the house. Mounting considerations depend on what your rooftop is like. Some things to keep in mind are:

When putting it up, make sure it's in such a position that if something slips, it can't fall on a power line.

Make sure the tower is sturdy—you may need to cement it in the ground and use guy wires to hold it up. When using guy wires on towers with beam antennas, make sure to have them attached to the tower far enough below the beam to permit rotation. Use good galvanized steel wire and an "egg" type insulator spaced every five feet along the guy wire until the wire reaches 25 feet down from the antenna. Past that you don't need to use insulators. This will keep them from interfering with the radiation of the antenna.

Also, it helps if your antenna is as clear as possible from other buildings, trees, or metallic objects. Large metallic objects within 17 feet can interfere with your antenna.

Small antennas like ground planes or three element beams can be supported on push-up type poles with guy wires. A push-up pole is made up of four or more sections of pipe, which telescopes up to about 50 feet or less. The sections are attached together by clamps or bolts. You attach your antenna to the top section, put the pole on the ground, and extend and clamp one section of pipe at a time, straight up. Tape your coax and rotating cable as the pole goes up. You'll usually need a step ladder and some help from your friends.

Larger antennas, including beams, should be supported by a triangular tower or telephone pole. Triangular towers are available in many models. Most of them come in ten foot sections that bolt together. Some are free standing; they don't need guy wires or support if they are cemented into the ground. Check manufacturer's specifications.

One common method of supporting a tower is to mount it against one wall of a house or building. Be sure to anchor into a strong part of the building, and keep in mind that your tower may be subjected to high winds and stress. Another way is to mount it up next to a large tree. Tower construction usually involves the help of some experienced people.

Rotators

A rotator is an electric motor that allows you to turn your beam in whatever direction you want. TV type rotators should only be used with the smallest of beams, three elements or less.

For the larger beams, you will need a heavy-duty rotator made especially for CB or ham use. They come with a control box which is wired to the rotator by an electric cable. Make sure to get your cable long enough to reach from your antenna to your radio, with some to spare in case you might want to move the position of your radio. The rotator is normally mounted on the tower a few feet below the top. It has a pipe called the *mast*, which goes up through a hole or sleeve on the top of the tower. The mast should be made of thick wall galvanized pipe 1¾" or bigger.

Test your rotator on the ground before you put it up on the tower. Hook it up according to manufacturer's directions. After checking to see if the rotator rotates in a full circle, set it on north. Then turn off the power and disconnect the leads. While putting up the antenna, make sure that your beam is pointed north—that way, your indicator and your antenna will match up. Make sure to leave enough slack in your coax between the tower and the mast to allow the antenna to rotate freely. You need to leave a little slack on your rotator cable, too, to prevent it from pulling on the connections. Both coax and rotator cables should be taped to one leg of the tower. These cables should not be brought away from the tower until you get at least ten feet below the beam.

JOURNEY TO THE BOTTOM OF YOUR RIG

CHAPTER 5

Okay, folks, it's time for a relaxed tour of your C.B. radio. We'll take our time, but we're not going to get bogged down in details. This "inside view" should give you a ballpark idea of how a radio actually works.

Let's go over here to the antenna. Let's grab it up top by that ball at the end and slide down the antenna into the rig. This is like *Fantastic Voyage!* Oops—watch your step around that coil; it's humming with juice! Okay, now that we're all together, everyone look down at your copy of the tour map through this section of the rig called the *receiver*.

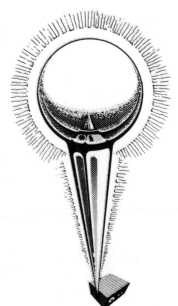

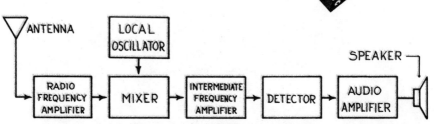

Our radio frequency slides down the antenna into a *Radio Frequency Amplifier*, where the signal is made a lot stronger. From maybe a few millionths of a volt, our signal jumps to a tenth of a volt or so. When I'm talking about a radio frequency in the Citizen's Band, I mean a regular wave with a frequency of 27 million cycles per second. That means that 27 million waves, 30 feet long, radiate from your antenna each second, traveling at the speed of light. This can be represented by waves like this:

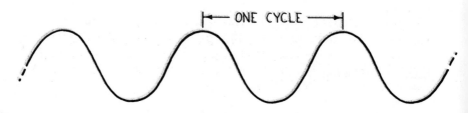

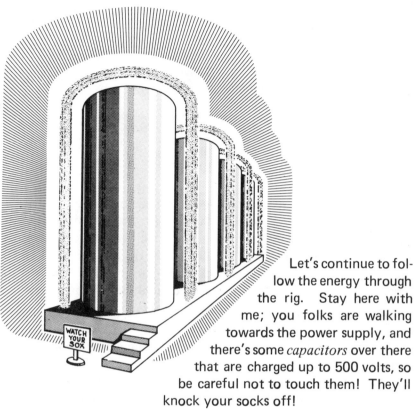

WATCH YOUR SOX

Let's continue to follow the energy through the rig. Stay here with me; you folks are walking towards the power supply, and there's some *capacitors* over there that are charged up to 500 volts, so be careful not to touch them! They'll knock your socks off!

Old-fashioned radios used to take the amplified high frequency signal we've got now and "peel" the voice frequencies right off it. But newer radios first reduce the incoming frequency to an *intermediate frequency*. This frequency is 455 thousand cycles per second. That's quite a step down from 27 million! The reason for an intermediate frequency is that it helps your receiver give clearer reception.

That's the "why" of intermediate frequency. The "how" is that we run the signal through a *mixer circuit*, where we also shoot in another high frequency signal:

These two signals mix together and produce a third signal, just like mixing red and blue paint together will give you purple. This third frequency is the intermediate frequency. Mixing two signals like that is called *heterodyning*.

By the way, that second frequency is made by a circuit called a *local oscillator*; *local* because the signal is made right in your rig as opposed to the incoming signal which comes from tens, hundreds, or even thousands of miles away. It's also an *oscillator* because electricity oscillates back and forth in this circuit. It goes back and forth so fast that it becomes a radio frequency.

So, now we have a much slower signal coming out of the mixer, at usually 455 thousand cycles a second. Once again we kick up the voltage by running this frequency through an I.F. (intermediate frequency) amplifier, which also purifies the signal and selects just the frequency we want. It surely is easier to amplify a signal at 455 thousand cycles a second than 27 million, for sure!

We're most all the way through our receiver now. If y'all want to rest, you can sit down on those resistors over there. Warm, ain't they? That's because some juice goes through them and *resistors* just use juice up as heat. So, get comfortable while I tell ya about the next mind-boggling circuit!

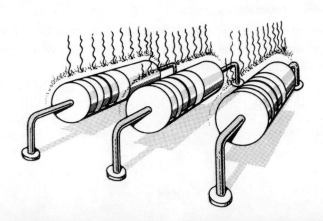

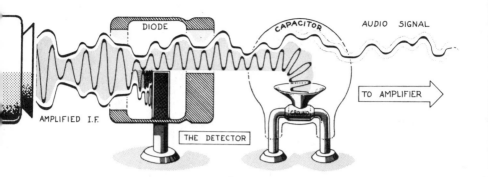

AMPLIFIED I.F.   DIODE   CAPACITOR   AUDIO SIGNAL   THE DETECTOR   GROUND   TO AMPLIFIER

This little beauty is called a *detector* and its job is to take the audio signal off of that I.F. frequency that we just saw amplified. The audio is contained in the I.F. frequency just like it was in the original radio signal that came in the antenna behind us. We reduced the incoming signal to an intermediate frequency, but that didn't affect the voice frequencies at all. This detector has the ability to pass all the voice energy on and discard the radio frequency energy. The radio signal brought the voice through the ozone but now that we got it, we have no further use for it.

That's why the radio frequency energy is called a *carrier*—because the voice is the information, and once it is delivered, the carrier has served its purpose. It's like when you bring home a pizza from the take-out place: it's the goodies that you're interested in, not the container.

Coming out at the far side of the detector is a voice signal, just like when it left the mouth of the person transmitting to you. We then run this audio signal through an audio amplifier or two so it's comfortably loud, and then it goes right into a speaker where the signal is turned from electrical waves back into sound waves that we can hear. Now before any of you go slipping out the speaker and onto the floor, let's turn and go back into the radio, and find out how this contraption transmits.

RELAY

Everybody rested up from going through the receiver? We're actually over halfway done, because a lot of the circuits we've walked through do double duty in both the transmit and receive parts of the trip.

We're sitting in the right place to start, since this time we'll follow the juice back from the microphone that's connected to that black cord we see running over the circuit board. See that big plastic container over there? That's the *relay*. The relay is a kind of switch which connects either the transmit or the receive circuits together. It's controlled by the push button on the microphone. That's how the parts common to both transmit and receive are switched back and forth from one to the other.

Okay, everybody. Let's take a gander at our tour map so we all know where we're going. Let's stay together and not get lost through all these twists and turns.

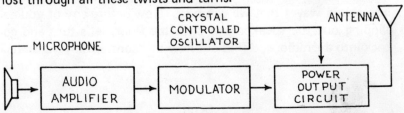

The amplifier that the microphone talks into is probably the same audio amplifier you use in your receiver. I'll bet that if you've got a *transceiver,* which is a transmitter and a receiver in one handy squawkbox, that it uses a lot of circuits for both sections. After all, transmitting is just receiving in reverse. Walk over here with me to this bunch of glowing electrical machinery.

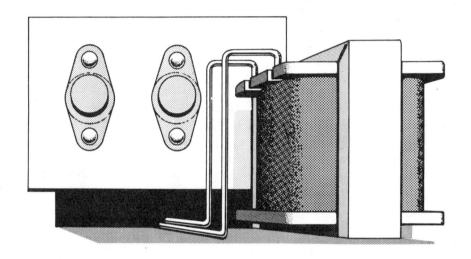

This here is the *modulator,* and it's another audio amplifier. "Modulation" is detection in reverse: we mix our voice signal with the radio frequency signal which will carry it out into the air. It doesn't matter how much we amplify an audio signal, it just won't radiate off your antenna, it's too low a frequency. That's why we need a carrier, and we'll see how it is produced in a minute.

I'll have to ask you kids over there not to spill your soft drinks on the circuit board—you'll make everything sticky and the guy who owns this rig we're walking through won't know *what's* happening the next time he opens it up!

If you'll look where I'm pointing, that's where the radio frequency is produced. That circuit is called the *crystal-controlled oscillator.* That square tin can over there contains a sliver of quartz crystal which puts out only one frequency, determined by the thickness of the crystal.

A crystal is just what it says. It is a piece of quartz crystal (a "rock") in a can. It operates on the same principle as a tuning fork. When you hit a tuning fork, it will vibrate at a particular frequency. The tone or frequency depends on how the tuning fork is constructed. A crystal operates in a similar way. When hit with the application of electricity, the crystal will vibrate at a frequency. Depending on how the crystal is cut, the frequency will vary.

Some rigs have up to 23 crystals to transmit on every CB channel. Other rigs save a lot of space (and money) by using only a few crystals and running the frequencies they produce through some fancy mixing circuits so as to get all 23 channels. Pretty fancy, huh? This circuit is called a *synthesizer.*

The voltage put out by a crystal vibrating is very small, a few millionths of a volt. The signal generated by the crystal gets boosted by another part of the oscillator so that it has enough voltage to drive the power amplifier. The modulator over there makes the juice in the power amplifier change with your voice. The power amplifier is where your carrier gets kicked up to that 5 watts to go out the antenna plug.

Well, here we are again at the antenna. We've kinda gone all the way through this maze and come all the way back round to the beginning. That power amplifier was the last circuit.

Now everybody get ready. We're getting out on the antenna now and we're about to leap on out there into the sky. We'll radiate on out there, travel at 186,000 miles per second for thousands of miles out into the Universe, ending up heaven knows where.

Chapter 6

TALKIN' SKIP

KBD 1007 mobile to base. You on the channel, Honey Bunny? Over.

You got the Honey Bunny base. Is that you, Big Dummy? Come on.

10-4, Honey Bunny. I'm headed....

HOW ABOUT IT SKIPLAND!!!   THE ONE FLORIDA ALLIGATOR, WE TRYIN' FER YA BREAK, BREAK!

Mercy sakes, Big Dummy—somebody's walkin' all over you. When are you....

10-4 NORTHERN CALIFORNIA!   YOU'RE SOUNDING CHOICE DOWN HERE IN THE BIKINI STATE FER SURE!

Why do stations from all parts of the country suddenly appear on the air and then vanish later as mysteriously as they rolled in? To answer this question, we need to understand how radio waves travel.

Radio waves mainly travel in straight lines like beams of light. Energy from the sun causes a layer of the atmosphere around the earth, called the ionosphere, to become electrically charged. This layer may be located anywhere from 25 to 250 miles above the earth. Its height at any given moment depends on the sea-

All mouth and no ears.

son, the time of day, the temperature of the earth, and the intensity of the sun. It reflects the radio waves much like a mirror reflects a beam of light. The higher the ionosphere, the greater the distance skipped. If the layers are not charged very strongly, the waves may pass on through and not be reflected back to earth. If it is strong, the signal may bounce once, hit the earth and bounce again, really getting far out there.

On CB, radio waves normally bounce about 500 miles or more. They don't usually bounce off the ionosphere any closer than that because the radio waves just go right on through at higher angles.

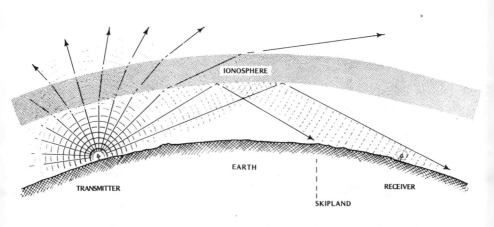

Usually the skip is best when the sun is about halfway between the two stations—so you'll usually hear skip from the east in midmorning and from the west in the afternoon. North-and-south skip can happen at any time of the day.

Sunspots or storms on the sun's surface greatly affect how frequently skip occurs. The more sunspots there are, the more skip there is. The number of sunspots on the sun goes up and down in an eleven year cycle. The last peak was in late 1969, and the next peak will occur in 1980.

With the number of CB radios in use today, there's lots of people transmitting on all the channels at the same time across the country. When the skip rolls in, usually there's a lot of noise that comes from so many stations being on the air at once. The squeals, whistles, and bumblebees you hear when two or more stations are transmitting on the same channel at once are called *heterodyne*. The only way to be heard above the heterodyne is to get louder than the rest of the stations. Most stations that you  hear doing this will be using very large antennas and illegal power amplifiers, sometimes called linear amplifiers (linears, shoes, kickers, afterburners, little boxes, power boosters, etc.).

Linears are hooked in the coaxial line between the radio and the antenna. These can be mobile units (usually 30 to 300 watts) or base (up to 1 kilowatt or so).

Currently the skip conditions are good on CB only during a few hours of the day. In a few years, the CB band will be open to skiptalkers all day long! It will cause interference with local communications to a much greater extent than it now does. This is the main reason that the FCC has made both skip talking and linears illegal—so that local communications can be maintained without interference. Also, this is why most new frequencies proposed for CB are located in the UHF (ultra high frequency) or VHF (very high frequency) spectrum, where the radio waves are too short to skip off the ionosphere (they just kind of slip on through).

If you really want to talk skip, consider getting a ham license. Hams are permitted to run up to a kilowatt of power with no limits or restrictions on antennas. Also, wider and less crowded bands of frequencies are available to hams. After all, CB is only one tiny niche of the RF spectrum.

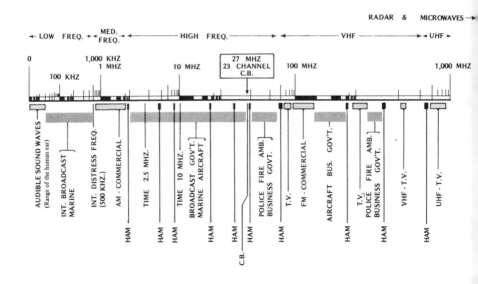

Radio Frequency Spectrum

A Kilowatt ham station

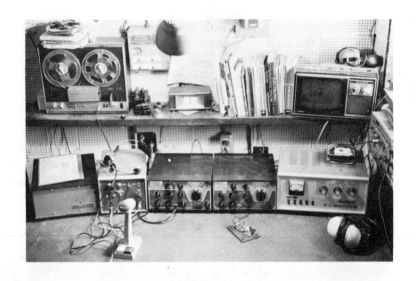

To get a ham license, you have to pass a test on radio theory, rules and regulations, and Morse code. Hams are expected to know enough to operate a high-powered station safely and keep from broadcasting signals that could interfere with other radio services. The FCC rules and regulations concerning radio are

based on some international agreements made in Geneva about thirty years ago. Books and study materials such as code tapes are available. It usually takes a month or two of study to get a license. Also, classes are sometimes held at local ham radio clubs, sometimes free of charge. The amateur bands are the gateway to instantaneous planetary communications.

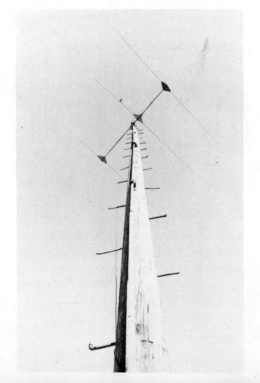

CHAPTER 7
GIZMOS

Power Microphones

A power mike has a built-in preamplifier. Most of them have a volume control built into the case that you can adjust according to how loud you talk. Power mikes usually come as optional equipment and need to have a connector wired onto the cord to fit your radio. A good power mike can sometimes increase the modulation or loudness of almost any CB. Some newer transceivers  have a built-in circuit that limits your modulation to 100%. Most power mikes use a crystal-type microphone element which has certain audio qualities that tend to "cut through" better than regular dynamic microphones. They usually run on a small battery inside the microphone. This battery usually lasts from six months to a year.

A power mike cannot increase the power of your transmitter above its 5-watt rating. It only adds more "punch" to your voice. When using a power mike you should get an on-the-air check to see how it sounds and adjust the volume control for the best sound while someone is listening to you. If you turn it up too high your voice will sound fuzzy, or you may get reports of squealing or breaking up.

Power mikes are available in base or mobile types, with 2 or 3 transistor preamplifiers. Usually 2 transistor preamplifiers are sufficient to modulate any transmitter. When purchasing a power mike, remember to also get a connector to fit the radio. The connector will need to be soldered on the end of the power mike's cord to match your particular transceiver. Power microphone manufacturers print pamphlets that include the wiring diagrams for almost all commercial transceivers. Make sure to check the pamphlet before purchasing a microphone to see if it is compatible with your transceiver.

SWR, Power & Modulation

These are meters that allow you to check how your antenna is working and how much power your transmitter is putting out. Just about any SWR meter, regardless of cost, can give you a pretty good idea of how well your antenna system is tuned up. Refer to the chapter on mobiles for directions on using an SWR meter. (Pages 46-47.) An SWR meter measures the relative power going to your antenna (forward) as compared to the power being lost in heat from your antenna or coax (reflected) due to your antenna being out of whack.

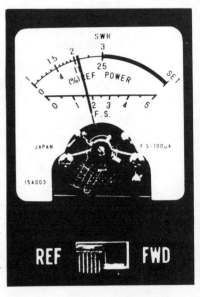

A power meter reads the amount of power that your transmitter is putting out in watts (usually about 3 watts). These meters are only accurate when used with an antenna that has a very low SWR. As with an SWR meter, the meter is connected between the output of the transceiver and the antenna. A short piece of coaxial cable, with a coax plug on both ends, is used to link the meter and the transceiver.

A modulation meter measures approximately the modulation of your transmitter. It is similar to the SWR and power meters. Some meters combine SWR, power or modulation into one meter.

Speech Compressors, Range Boosters, and Audio Limiters

These are gizmos that you plug the microphone into, and that you plug into your rig's mike input. They boost up your voice when you talk soft and cut it down when you talk loud. They make it so that you can modulate your transmitter with the highest average modulation possible. If adjusted properly, they will cut down on overmodulation and pack more punch into your signal.

Antenna Switches

An antenna switch usually comes in a small box that can be mounted some place near your radio. You plug the coaxial lead-in from different antennas into the switch and run a short coax jumper to the transceiver. These are very handy when using a beam and a vertical antenna. You can monitor on the vertical and switch over to the beam to make a connection with a particular station.

Dummy loads

A dummy load is a device that can take the place of an antenna for testing purposes. It plugs into the antenna jack on your rig and you can transmit without going out over the air. A dummy load is nothing more than a 50-ohm resistor. Small light bulbs are sometimes used as dummy loads. They should not be used on transistorized equipment, and are not recommended for tube equipment, either.

Tone squelch

Tone squelch is available as optional equipment for some transceivers. It cuts off your receiver's volume and puts it on standby until another radio equipped with tone squelch of the same type triggers your receiver to come on. The advantage of that is that you don't have to sit and listen to other stations on a channel in order to monitor for someone else with the same tone squelch. It's a private signaling device.

Phone patches

A phone patch can prove to be fairly handy. It allows you to hook your CB radio up to your telephone. For example, if you were driving your car and needed to get a message across town to someone on the telephone, you could call back to your base and have someone there turn on the phone patch and dial the number you want to call. You could then speak directly over the telephone via CB. This requires someone at the base station to press the mike button when the party on the phone talks.

TVI Filter — (How to Stay at Peace with the Neighbors)

Folks who are into radio encounter one problem quite frequently: that is having their CB radio interfere with TV reception in the neighborhood, causing distortion of the picture and sound when you transmit. Now, most CBs will not bother a properly built TV unless they are fairly close to one another. However, some TVs have a front end that is not selective enough to reject a strong nearby CB signal. And occasionally a radio out of adjustment will radiate interference with its regular signal that will mess up a TV. If possible, moving the CB antenna and the TV antenna further apart will sometimes clear it up. If this doesn't do it, you can get a low-pass filter that plugs in between your CB and your antenna. These are available at most radio supply houses. If the interference persists, try putting a high-pass filter on the TV set. This filter is installed on the antenna leads of the TV set. You disconnect the wires connecting the TV antenna to the back of the TV set and connect them to the terminals on the high-pass filter. Then connect the leads from the high-pass filter to the TV set.

Antenna Matchers

Antenna matchers are useful when you have an antenna that has a high SWR. They can prevent the high SWR from damaging the final power amplifier of your transmitter. You'll get out much better if you use an antenna that has a low SWR than if you try to match a bad antenna system with one of these. Antenna matchers do not improve the SWR at the antenna—they only make it so that the high SWR does not reach the transmitter.

Receiver Preamps or Boosters

These usually come in a box that plugs in between your antenna and your transceiver. They amplify all the signals coming into your receiver. These are especially good for older-model transceivers that lack volume or sensitivity on receive. Usually they're not necessary for the new 23-channel transistorized transceivers, which have ample sensitivity.

Bilateral Amplifiers

This is a combination of a receiver preamp and a linear amplifier. In other words, it works both ways. It helps on receive and transmit.

Gooney Birds

This is a small box with a speaker that has a built-in oscillator. It is held up to the microphone or sometimes installed in the transmitter. When used on the air it sounds like a slide whistle or an electronic bird call. It's used to attract attention and has recently been banned for use on CB by the FCC.

CHAPTER 8

Fixing Your Rig
or
What Went Wrong?

If something goes wrong with your rig, there are quite a few things that you can do to make it work again or to find out what's wrong with it.

One thing you have to keep in mind when working with CBs or any kind of electrical equipment is Safety First. All CB radios that run off of house current have high voltage in them. Definitely enough to croak you. So take it easy and pay good attention.

You can't hurt yourself with the voltages in an 12-volt mobile transistor rig, but you can burn out the rig if you're not careful. Tube type mobile rigs have high voltage inside, even when operated off of a car battery.

There are certain safety precautions that you need to know if you're going to take the cover off your radio:

Never take the cover off the radio with the power cord plugged in. This includes 12-volt transistorized rigs.

Move any metal objects or wires out from around or under the radio when testing or working on it.

Never turn on the rig without the correct fuse in the fuse holder.

Don't operate your rig during a lightning storm.

Don't touch any components inside the radio while the power is connected.

Don't touch or turn on the radio if it or you are wet.

Most of the time the different problems that come up with CB rigs are external to the rig itself—such as the antenna, microphone, connectors and wires.

The FCC says that only technicians with a 1st or 2nd class commercial license can legally repair any frequency-determining or power output circuits. This is to prevent you from accidentally tuning your radio up off frequency or above the legal power limit.

TROUBLE-SHOOTING GUIDE

RECEIVING

Symptoms	What to Do
1. No dial lights, no receive, set is dead.	1. Is it plugged in? Check to see if power switch is on. Check to see if fuse is blown. If it is, replace it with another fuse of the same rating. Don't use aluminum foil. Check for possible frayed wires or skinned off insulation If it is a mobile, sometimes the ignition key must be on for the rig to get its juice. Check connections where the rig gets its power. Check ground connection.
2. Can receive but cuts in and out. Dial lights blink.	2. Intermittent connection to power or battery. Check fuse holder. Check ground connection. Make sure that screws are tight on all mounts. Wiggle power cord and antenna coaxial cable—see if it makes the power cut on and off. Check power plug on transceiver.

Symptoms	*What to Do*
3. Dial lights come on, but no receive.	3. Check squelch knob and make sure the mike cord is plugged in. Make sure PA switch is in CB position. Wiggle microphone cord and connector. If it cuts in and out, there might be a loose connection in the connector or mike. In this case, the mike cord might need to be cut off and re-soldered.
4. Receiving only very nearby stations.	4. Is the antenna connected? How is SWR? If the SWR is high, possibly there is a short in the coax or connectors. Check local-distant switch—should be in distant position. Check RF gain knob, it should be all the way up. If it is a tube unit, check the tubes.
5. Receiving only hiss.	5. Check antenna and connector. Take antenna connector off and put it back on again. If that makes any difference in the hiss, try other channels and a radio check with a nearby station.

Symptoms	*What to Do*
6. Fuse blows when rig is turned on.	6. Short or blown transistor inside radio. Check to see if screws or mounting bolts are touching any components or wires inside the radio. Do not replace the fuse with a larger fuse or aluminum foil. This can cause further damage to radio.
7. Stations received move S-meter, but do not come on through speaker clearly or not at all.	7. Check squelch knob. If speaker sounds fuzzy, try plugging an external speaker in. If this works, you might have to replace speaker. Check wires leading to speaker inside radio. Could be bad audio transistor.
8. Nearby stations sound fuzzy.	8. If they're within 100 feet, this might be normal. Try switching local-distant switch to local, or turning RF gain down.

Symptoms	*What to Do*
9. Smoke comes out of top of rig when turned on.	9. By all means turn it off!! Pull the plug. Check to see what size fuse is in the fuse holder. It should be no more than 6 amps for a tube radio and no more than 3 amps for a transistorized radio. Check the polarity of the battery connections in a mobile. Check to see that the negative and positive wires are hooked up right. If you are using an external speaker, make sure that none of the wires leading to it touch the chassis of the radio or the body of your vehicle. After disconnecting radio from the power, replace the fuse with one of the proper value. Check to see if any screws or mounting bolts touch components inside radio. If the polarity was reversed, try out the rig again. If the fuse blows again, there is probably a blown diode or transistor.
10. Receiver just hums.	10. Microphone not plugged in. If radio uses external power supply, it might be blown. Try radio on a car battery or another DC power supply. If it's a tube unit, there might be a tube or capacitor out.

TRANSMITTING

Symptoms	What To Do
1. When mike button is pushed, receiver does not cut out—cannot transmit.	1. Check microphone cord and microphone switch. The cord might have pulled some of the wires loose in the connector. These can just be resoldered to the proper pins inside the connector. If radio has a relay, it might need to be replaced or cleaned.
2. Transmits a carrier, but no modulation.	2. If you can receive OK, the problem is probably in the microphone or cord. Check PA–CB switch.
3. No carrier, no modulation.	3. Could be crystal. Check mike cord. Try different channels.
4. One or more channels not working.	4. Crystal or crystal oscillator is not working. Could be channel selector switch.

Symptoms	What to Do
5. Fuse blows when transmitting.	5. Blown power transistor. Screws or bolts possibly shorting against components inside of radio. Short in antenna connector or antenna.
6. Only getting out ¼ mile or so. Relative power meter reads zero.	6. Check antenna and coax cable SWR. Antenna load and plate adjustment screws might need to be set. If all these are OK, final transistor might be blown. Have it replaced.
7. Transmitter "breaking up." Choppy transmission.	7. Probably a loose connection somewhere. If it only does it on transmit, it's probably the microphone or cord. If on transmit and receive, it might be the antenna or coax cable. Check the ground on the antenna.
8. Squealing on transmit.	8. Loose wire in microphone or cord. If you are using a power mike, try turning it down slightly. If this doesn't help, try a new battery in it. Make sure that the aluminum foil shielding in the power mike is in place right if you change the battery.

Symptoms	*What to Do*
9. Your voice heard from speaker when transmitting. Howling.	9. Check the PA–CB switch. Also check external speaker wires and PA speaker wires to see if they're grounding out to the body of the vehicle or radio. Also check for shorts in microphone or connector.
10. Weak modulation.	10. If you're using a crystal microphone, the mike element might need to be replaced. Tube or transistor blown.
11. Modulation distorted.	11. Power mike up too high. Antenna out of whack. Mike gain up too high. Microphone might need to be replaced.

Note– Sometimes a loose tube or crystal can prevent your rig from working properly. So check all plug-in parts to make sure they fit snugly in place.

Some radios, usually older models, have open relays. Dirty contacts can prevent a radio from switching from transmit to receive. Clean the contacts using a burnishing tool or by pulling a dollar bill through them while holding them lightly together.

Repairing Microphone & Antenna Connections

You need some basic tools:

—Soldering iron
—Rosin-core solder (60/40)
—Small pliers (needlenose)
—Medium wirecutters
—Screwdrivers
—Knife

Tips on Soldering

All electrical soldering is done with rosin-core (not acid-core) solder. Acid-core tends to corrode electrical connections. You can test to see if the soldering iron is hot enough by touching the solder to the tip. It should melt easily. It's a good idea to practice on a couple of wires before trying to solder your microphone cable.

When soldering wires, it's a good idea to tin the wires before soldering. You tin the wire by heating the end of the wire up with the iron and applying a small amount of solder to the iron and the wire—just enough to put a thin coat on the wire. Make sure not to melt the plastic insulation while doing this.

Attach or stick the wire in the terminal you want to solder it to. The connector and wire should be held as steady as possible while soldering. When you solder, put the tip of your iron so that it rests on the wire and the terminal at the same time, and apply enough solder for it to flow over the wire and terminal evenly. Never apply any more solder than is necessary to hold it good. Don't move the connection until you're sure the solder has set. It should be nice and shiny.

Microphone Connections

The microphone cord, with all its pulling and moving around, is often a source of trouble. Sometimes a wire comes loose inside the connector where it plugs into the rig. Sometimes, due to flexing, a wire will even break inside the cord where you can't see it, especially at the points where it goes into the connector or the microphone. You can usually tell when this is the case by transmitting, holding the microphone steady, and wiggling the mike cord in various places.

To check the microphone connector, find a flat clean surface to take it apart on. For some connectors you will need a small jeweler's or Phillips head screwdriver. Take out all the screws in the connector and put them in a safe place. Then take apart the two halves of the connector, or the cover, depending on the type of connector. If one of the wires is broken off of one of the pins of the connectors, it's sometimes possible just to solder it back onto the pin. Make sure that it does not touch any of the other pins or bare wires.

Sometimes it may be necessary to cut the cord off and resolder the whole thing. Cut it off about an inch back from the connector. Then cut the outer jacket back three-quarters of an inch from the end of the cable, being very careful not to nick the insulation on any of the wires inside the cable. Unwind the outer braided shield from around the inner wires and twist the small wires of the shield tightly together. Strip one-eighth of an inch of insulation off the tips of the inner wires and tin these tips as well as the twisted tip of the shield.

Now you're ready to solder the wire to the connector. Be sure you have slipped the outer covering or case of the connector over the cable before soldering (depends on type of connector). Now take one of the old wires off of one of the  pins of the connector and resolder the new wire of the same color to that pin. Do all the rest of the wires the same way. Be sure you have the right colors on the right pins. The pins are usually numbered right on the connector. Make sure no stray strands of wire touch any other pins or the metal case.

Now you're ready to reassemble the connector case. Make sure the cable clamp firmly grips the outer jacket of the mike cord, taking all the strain off the connections.

Trouble in the Mike

If you find that your trouble is where the cord goes into the microphone, carefully cut the cord an inch or two down from the microphone and resolder the connections, paying very careful attention to where they go—similar to the method used to solder the mike connector.

For some more complicated microphones, such as power mikes, this could be more difficult, because you can't get at the connections as good. You might want to have this done by an electronics repairman.

Antenna Connections

The antenna is another place where a lot of times the connections go bad, due to weathering and movement. The most common antenna problems are in the coaxial lines and its connectors. An insulator at the base of an antenna can break or wear out and cause a short. Sometimes a temporary repair can be made with electrical tape.

Also, if the coax cable is run through an open window or door, the line can get crimped or cut. In this case, if there is enough excess coax, you can cut off the cable at the break and reconnect it to the antenna.

Soldering Coax Connectors

The most common coaxial connector on most rigs is called a PL259. It comes apart into three separate pieces.

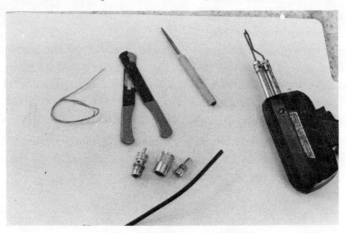

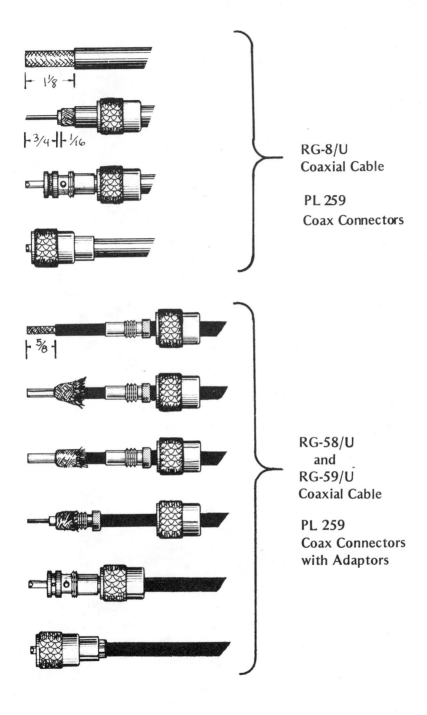

RG-8/U
Coaxial Cable

PL 259
Coax Connectors

RG-58/U
  and
RG-59/U
Coaxial Cable

PL 259
Coax Connectors
with Adaptors

Slip adaptor and outer cylinder over cable.

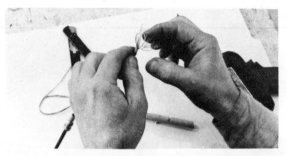

Strip outer insulation back 1¼ inches. Separate strand of braided shield very carefully; don't cut or break any of them off.

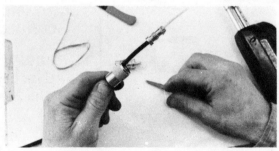

Slide adaptor up to end of black outer insulation and bend the shield down over it. Then cut the shield so that it doesn't extend down over the threads of the adaptor.

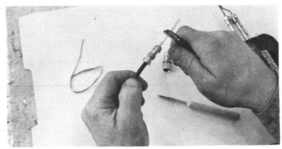

Strip the insulation off the center conductor of the coax, leaving a little more than ¼ inch of insulation next to the adaptor.

Slip the remaining part over the inner conductor and adapter, and screw on the adapter. Solder the inner conductor on the tip of the connector. Let the solder flow into the hole a little bit. Cut the inner conductor off flush with the tip.

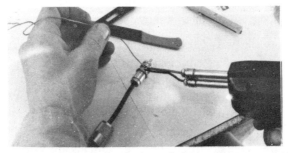

Hold soldering gun on the holes of the connector until it gets good and hot. Apply solder to the iron and hole. Don't use too much solder. You'll have to slip the outside of the connector over this solder joint. Be careful not to heat up the connector or coax cable to the extent that you melt the insulation.

Phased Lock Loop

This is a circuit that uses integrated circuits (IC chips) to take the place of many crystals to select the channels. With the use of a two knob digital channel selector, this allows the possibility of many more than 23 channels when approved by the FCC.

23 Channel Synthesizer Crystals

Most new 23-channel rigs are synthesized. This means that they use only a few crystals to make all the channels. The crystal frequencies are added and subtracted together in order to use fewer crystals. Usually if a crystal goes bad, in a synthesized unit it will make 4 or 5 channels not work. Sometimes the manual that came with the radio will list the numbers on the crystals for the channels they are used on. These can be re-ordered from the manufacturer. They should be installed by a licensed repairman.

Crystals

Crystals for most rigs plug into little sockets, and it's as easy as plugging in a lamp. The only thing is, make sure you have the right crystal for your rig. They come in several sizes and styles for different radios, so be sure to check the frequency. Even if they say the right channel number, they still may be the wrong type for your particular rig. So check the frequency of your transmit and receive crystals and buy similar crystals for replacement. You can have crystal frequencies looked up for you in a parts replacement book in a parts store.

Most rigs that have less than 23 channels use two crystals for each channel. One crystal is used for transmitting and the other for receiving. The most common types use a receive crystal that is 455 kilohertz less than the transmit crystal. The way to find out if your rig uses this type of crystal is to subtract the frequency of the receive crystal from the frequency of the transmit crystal of the same channel. The frequencies are usually stamped in the metal case of the crystal. This kind of crystal is usually in the 26 to 28 MHz (Megahertz) range. Some older tube-type radios use crystals in the 13-megacycle range. Usually in this case, the receive crystal will be 222.5 kilohertz below the transmit crystal of the same channel. These are called ½-fundamental or overtone-type crystals.

Crystal Frequencies

Channel	Fundamental		½ Fundamental or Overtone	
	Transmit	Receive	Transmit	Receive
1	26.965	26.510	13.4825	13.255
2	26.975	26.520	13.4875	13.260
3	26.985	26.530	13.4925	13.265
4	27.005	26.550	13.5025	13.275
5	27.015	26.560	13.5075	13.280
6	27.025	26.570	13.5125	13.285
7	27.035	26.580	13.5175	13.290
8	27.055	26.600	13.5275	13.300
9	27.065	26.610	13.5325	13.305
10	27.075	26.620	13.5375	13.310
11	27.085	26.630	13.5425	13.315
12	27.105	26.650	13.5525	13.325
13	27.115	26.670	13.5625	13.330
14	27.125	26.670	13.5625	13.335
15	27.135	26.680	13.5675	13.340
16	27.155	26.700	13.5775	13.350
17	27.165	26.710	13.5825	13.355
18	27.175	26.720	13.5875	13.360
19	27.185	26.730	13.5925	13.365
20	27.205	26.750	13.6025	13.375
21	27.215	26.760	13.6075	13.380
22	27.225	26.770	13.6125	13.385
23	27.255	26.800	13.6275	13.400

Noise: How to get rid of it

The object of noise suppression is to capture those loose noises made by your vehicle's electrical system and run them into the ground before they have a chance to reach your receiver. These noises are usually created by sparks originating from your spark plugs, distributor, accessory motors, generator, regulator, or gauges. The sparks are electrical impulses that put out static much like little transmitters. There are various ways to keep these sparks from radiating energy that your receiver will pick up. Most of this kind of noise is picked up by the antenna. Most of the time in a car or a truck with a gasoline engine, the ignition system (spark plugs, distributor, ignition wires, and coil) causes most of the noise.

Ignition noise is recognized by a loud popping or crackling, increasing to a buzz when you rev up the motor. If you rev up your engine to a high speed and then shut the key off, the moment you shut it off the ignition noise should stop.

One of the best remedies for this kind of noise is to install radio resistance spark plug wires. These are available in almost all auto parts stores. Also, radio resistance type spark plugs will cut down ignition noise quite a lot. After installing these, the engine should be re-timed and tuned at a reputable garage. If you're already using them and still get a lot of noise, you might need to suppress other sources of noise.

Another source of noise is the generator. There are various kinds of suppressors available for generators and alternators. They're available almost everywhere CBs are sold. Generator noise sounds like a whine that varies with the engine's speed. Usually, a suppressor-capacitor in the armature lead of the generator or an alternator noise suppressor in the battery lead of the alternator clears up the whine.

Noise is sometimes caused by heater and wiper motors and gauges. This kind of noise can be easily remedied by the addition of a coaxial capacitor. This is the kind that's found in most radio stores—it has two screw terminals. Sometimes it might be necessary to drill a hole somewhere close to the motor or the gauge to mount it.

To hook it up you cut the hot wire leading to the motor and strip off the insulation ¼ inch back. Then connect the two ends you now have to the two screw terminals on the capacitor.

Noise from the ignition system occasionally comes through the wires leading to the radio. The noise is picked up in the engine compartment or on the battery leads and channeled to the radio by the wires. In this case, an RF choke and capacitor should be used on the hot lead going to the CB. Also coaxial cable can be run up to the battery, grounding the shield and using the inner conductor to run juice to the rig. Make sure to use an in-line fuse where it attaches to the battery connection.

Another kind of static is caused by bare wires or loose connections shorting or arcing to the frame or other wires in the vehicle. This is usually noticed on bumpy roads. One way to find which wires are doing this is to listen on the radio with the engine stopped, ignition switch on. Wiggle wires under the dash and in the engine compartment. If any static is found, tape up or repair the wires.

The regulator is another frequent cause of static. It's usually noticed as a clicking or intermittent popping sound. When the engine is just started up or when the headlights are turned on, it tends to come on stronger. To clear this up, make sure that the regulator case and mounting screws have a good electrical connection to the body. You may also need to add .1 µfd coaxial feed-through capacitors on the battery wire leading to the regulator. Caution: don't use this type of capacitor on the field connection of the regulator. There's a special kind of suppressor used on the field connection.

Generally, gasoline-powered vehicles will be a lot noisier than diesel-powered, because there are no spark plugs in a diesel engine. Spark plug, or ignition, noise is the main cause of static in an automobile. Even if you try all the suppression methods possible, you may not be able to cut down all of the spark plug noise without making your engine not work. But you should be able to cut it down quite a lot—enough to make listening enjoyable.

For the real rough cases, there are marine-type shielded ignition harnesses available. These will cut out almost all ignition noise from the spark plugs. They're fairly expensive, but they're very dependable. You would probably have to order them through a two-way communications outlet, or a marine engine distributor.

Here's one other thing that we've tried for cutting down static from the distributor: get a large-size tin can, big enough to just fit over the distributor. You can mount it down with a couple of angle brackets to the engine block. The can should be connected securely to the engine block to make a good ground. Make sure that your ignition wires are in good condition if you do this, because if they have any cracks in the insulation they will probably arc across to the can. You need to cut the bottom and top out of the can or make suitable holes for the ignition wires to come out of the top. Make sure you get the ignition wires back on the distributor in the proper order. There should be no sharp edges left on the can—these could wear through the ignition wires. We've experienced a drop in ignition noise by about half on some vehicles using this method.

VEHICLE NOISE SUPPRESSION

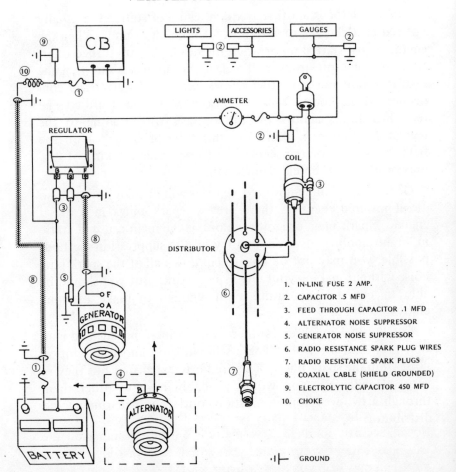

1. IN-LINE FUSE 2 AMP.
2. CAPACITOR .5 MFD
3. FEED THROUGH CAPACITOR .1 MFD
4. ALTERNATOR NOISE SUPPRESSOR
5. GENERATOR NOISE SUPPRESSOR
6. RADIO RESISTANCE SPARK PLUG WIRES
7. RADIO RESISTANCE SPARK PLUGS
8. COAXIAL CABLE (SHIELD GROUNDED)
9. ELECTROLYTIC CAPACITOR 450 MFD
10. CHOKE

⊣⊢   GROUND

IT'S TEN O:CLOCK...
DO YOU KNOW WHERE
YOUR RIG IS ?

Mobile CB radios just happen to be small, light, expensive, and easy to rip off. Here are some suggestions which may help prevent this from happening to you. You don't want to lose your ears, fer sure.

Your CB can be installed in such a way that you can easily remove it from under the dash and lock it in the trunk or take it into your house. One way to do this is to use a *slide mount*. This is the kind of mount that allows you to slide your rig in and out easily. These are available at most CB shops. If you prefer to have your radio in your mobile, you can get a *locking mount* that makes it so you need a key to take the rig off the mount. There are also easy-to-install car burglar alarm systems, available at electronics stores. Some burglar alarm systems honk your horn or ring an alarm inside your car when the door or hood is opened, or if your radio is taken from its mount. When you do leave it in your mobile, be sure to lock the doors.

All CB radios come with serial numbers on them. Keep a record of your serial number with your owner's manual. If you are about to buy a used rig, make sure the serial numbers have not been removed. Many electronic repair places will not work on rigs without their numbers.

Many police departments are suggesting that you etch your Social Securtiy number or your driver's license number on the case and back of your radio. They may even provide this service. This may help you recover your rig if it acquires some legs.

CHAPTER 9

Walkie-Talkies

Walkie-talkies have a variety of uses, depending on the requirements of the user and the power of the walkie-talkie itself. Some of the smaller and cheaper ones of the 100-milliwatt variety (or less) are sold as toys or for use at very close range. These are usually limited to a couple of blocks at the very most. Due to the receivers in them being not very selective, they will pick up just about any CB radio nearby, even if it doesn't happen to be on the same channel. There are better units available in the 100-milliwatt range (no license needed). Some of them come with two or more channels. Most of these are more selective and have a cleaner sound than the cheaper toys.

The next class of walkie-talkies is in the 250-milliwatt to 2-watt class. These are usually good for communication on a clear channel up to about a couple of miles at the most. They can be used for communication to a 5-watt mobile or base unit and will receive signals almost as well as a mobile unit. Usually this kind of walkie-talkie comes with one or two sets of crystals, and if it has any more channels than that, you have to get a set of crystals for each channel you want. They usually run off of eight or ten penlite batteries. It's best to use alkaline, mercury, or re-chargeable batteries, because regular batteries will run out quickly if you do a lot of transmitting.

Three to five-watt walkie-talkies are good for communications up to about five miles, maybe more, on a clear channel. They usually come with three or more channels. There are even 23-channel units available. Some of them have the kind of features you would expect in a good mobile unit: external antenna plug, PA, earphone and microphone plugs, squelch, etc.

Almost all CB walkie-talkies come with telescoping antennas, most of them about five feet long. When using one of these, you should remember to always have the antenna extended to its full length before transmitting. This is because the SWR will be too high when the antenna is down. There are add-on antennas that can be clamped to the stub of the telescoping antenna. These are usually short springy whips about a foot or two long, with a loaded coil in the base. These add-on antennas won't get out as far as the telescoping whip. They're useful for operating in close quarters where a five-foot antenna would get in the way.

If you break off one of the sections of the telescoping whip, about all you can do is replace the whole whip. This is easily done—there's just one screw holding it in at the base of the whip inside the walkie-talkie. Keep the insulating grommet in place when you put the new whip in. This will prevent it from shorting out to the case of the walkie-talkie.

For really dependable service a five-watt hand-held unit with about six channels and a metal case is about the best for all-around use. If you're a dedicated CBer who doesn't want to be without ears, this might be a good thing to get.

5-watt, 6-channel walkie-talkie with modified antenna

There are lots of antennas out on the market today—all kinds of different shapes and sizes. Because of this competitive market, antenna companies are always trying to put out a better product for a cheaper price. Commercially made antennas are usually easy to put up and maintain. However, you might want to try your hand at making an antenna. You can make an antenna out of readily available parts that will work as good or better than some commercially made antennas.

You'll need an SWR meter to check out the antenna after building it.

¼ Wave Ground Plane Antenna

This antenna consists of a driven element and four radial wires which act as a ground. The driven element receives the transmit energy from the rig.

Parts list:

102" piece of aluminum pipe or conduit, ¾ or 1" diam.	Rope, enough to guy the ground radials, depending on
Two U-bolts, same size as pipe	the height of the antenna
One sheet metal screw	a couple of two by fours
One J-hook	Electrical tape
Four "egg" ceramic insulators	Silicone sealer to cover coax
40' of 16 gauge wire	connection

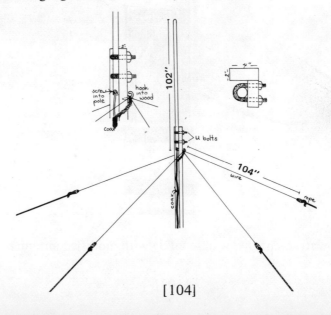

The inside conductor of the coax is connected to the aluminum pipe by means of a screw into the bottom of the pipe. See the detail drawing on preceding page. Coat this connection with sealer or cover it with tape to protect it from corrosion.

All vertical antennas need to be grounded in some way. A mobile antenna uses the car body as the ground. On this antenna, the four radial wires are used as the ground. This is called the ground plane of the antenna.

The braided wire which forms the outside conductor of the coax is soldered to all four radial wires. The wires must be exactly 104" long (¼ wavelength).

Remember that the inner conductor and outer braid of the coax must not touch each other, nor can the radials contact the driven element. The radials slope down at about a 45° angle in different directions, and are tied to the insulators. Rope or nylon cord is then tied to the insulators and used to hold the radials out. They can be attached to anywhere convenient— trees, fence, house, etc.

If you are short on room for such a radial system, you can use 104" pieces of aluminum tubing, or suspend the wires on PVC pipe, bamboo, or 1" x 2" wooden sticks. The sticks only need to be about 10 feet long. They can be attached forming an "x" at the base of the vertical element. The wires can hang off the ends a few feet.

It's a good idea to check the SWR when done. It should be lower than 2, and most likely lower than 1.5 or 1.3.

A ¼ wave ground plane made from wire can be suspended from a tree. We've talked to stations over 40 miles away using this antenna up about 30 feet high, running a mobile rig on a car battery into it.

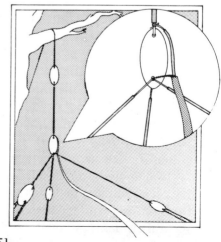

Coax Cable Vertical Antenna

A vertical dipole (½ wave) can be made right from the coax itself. You take your coax and very carefully, without nicking the braided shield, strip 102 inches of the outer insulation jacket off one end. After removing the outer jacket, start bunching the shield down the coax from the end. Now, where the outer jacket and shield meet, separate the braided shield enough to get the inner conductor out through the hole in the braid. Pull all of the inner conductor through and stretch it and the braid out. Be careful not to skin any of the insulation off the inner conductor. Now attach an antenna insulator to the end of the inner conductor. Measure the braided shield. Cut it off at about 106" and attach an antenna insulator to the end. The total length of the inner and outer conductor should be about 17 feet (½ wave). You can haul it up to any height you want with a string or rope attached to the insulator on the center conductor. It's a good idea to coat the end of the coax cable where it separates with some waterproof sealer. This keeps water from seeping into the coax, which could cause a high SWR.

Just attach a coax connector on the end of the coax going to your transceiver and you're on the air. The SWR should be 1.5 or better, if cut to the proper length. It'll get out about as good as a ¼ wave ground plane antenna if you get it up high and in the clear. Don't hoist this antenna up next to a metal pole, because the metal will interfere with the antenna's operation and make a high SWR.

Using a Mobile Antenna as a Base Antenna

With the mobile antenna, the metal body of the car serves as the ground for the antenna. Although most mobile antennas will not work as well as a regular ground plane antenna, you can turn a mobile antenna into a ground plane by adding 9' ground radials. The important thing here is that the ground radials should be connected to the ground side of the coax and must be insulated from making contact with the vertical element.

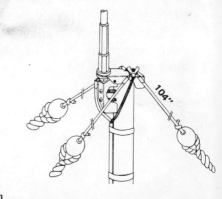

Fishing Pole Ear – A Homemade Mobile Antenna

Antenna Parts

One 7-foot fiberglass fishing pole with hollow base
One piece of steel rod 4 to 6 inches long—right diameter
    to slip into base of pole
One ¼" x 1" machine bolt (threads to match mount)
12 feet of enamel #18 gauge wire
Some good epoxy glue

Antenna Mount Parts

One ¼" x 2½" bolt and nut (same threads as bolt on base of
    pole
One longer-than-usual ¼" nut
Two plastic insulating washers
Three metal 5/8" diameter washers
One large terminal lug

First you got to get yourself a fishing pole, 6 to 9 feet long. If you already have an old one lying around, you can clip off the line loops and cut the handle off.

We did some shopping and found that a finished fishing pole as long as we wanted was as expensive as a new manufactured CB antenna. But then we discovered a sporting goods store that sold unfinished fiberglass poles 7 feet long for $6. The kind we found was a black hollow tapered pole about 5/8" inside diameter at the base.

The next step is to hook something to the pole so you can screw it to a mount on your vehicle.

The way we did it was to get a piece of scrap steel rod near the inside diameter of the base of the hollow pole. (If the pole ain't hollow you'll have to figure out another way of hooking to it.)

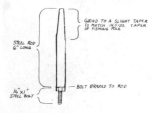

Grind a slight taper to match inside taper of fishing pole.

Braze bolt to rod. Use ¼" x 1" steel bolt.

Epoxy steel rod inside base of fishing pole.

Now it's time to get into the electrical part of the antenna. The fishing pole ain't the antenna; it's just to hold the wire up. We need to wind a wire around the fishing pole in a way that will make it in tune with the CB band.

Now you tightly wrap the wire in a spiral up from the base of the pole.   Make the distance between windings as wide as possible below and above the coil.

We used a 7 foot pole because that's what we found. The shorter length had the advantage of allowing it to be mounted right in the center of the roof and not be too high.

7' OVERALL

If your antenna is shorter than 9 feet, you can tune it by making a coil around the pole. To really tune an ear up right, you need to use a SWR meter, but if you follow these particular dimensions you should be near tuned up.   Different lengths of antenna will work, but different coil windings will be necessary, so if you have a different length pole you'll have to use a meter to tune it up. You just have to dive right in and try different numbers of coil windings. The longer the pole, the less center coil windings; the shorter, the more windings necessary. It takes playing around and trial and error.

FOUR TURNS RIGHT NEXT TO EACH OTHER

FOUR TURNS ½" APART

2'3"

We used enamel coated wire. It's easy to find in motor windings, generators, transformers, etc. It's best to use enamel wire so the coil turns can't possibly short to each other.

At the bottom, wrap the wire around the ¼" bolt. Be sure to scrape the enamel coating off the wire and clean the bolt for good contact. Solder that wire to the bolt or use a nut to hold the wire on the bolt.

We covered some antennas with a thin coat of fiberglass (which you can tint any color you want). They looked pretty good but the fiberglass chipped off some of the antenna tips that were mounted fairly high up. You can prevent chipping by putting some shrink tubing over the tip. Shrink tubing is another possible way to hold the wire on. It's available at electronics shops.

This antenna is rated at 300 watts continuous AM power.

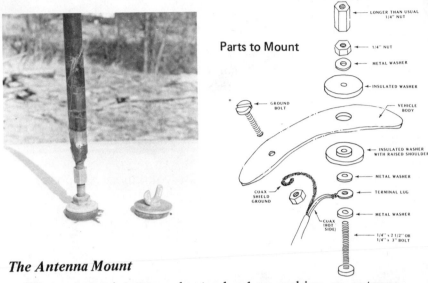

Parts to Mount

LONGER THAN USUAL 1/4" NUT

1/4" NUT

METAL WASHER

INSULATED WASHER

GROUND BOLT

VEHICLE BODY

INSULATED WASHER WITH RAISED SHOULDER

METAL WASHER

COAX SHIELD GROUND

TERMINAL LUG

METAL WASHER

COAX (HOT SIDE)

1/4" x 2 1/2" OR 1/4" x 3" BOLT

The Antenna Mount

The main point to understand when making an antenna mount is that the antenna itself is not supposed to ground out to the body of the vehicle. This means that the bolt the antenna hooks to must be insulated from the metal body.

Your homemade mount must use good insulating washers because if the bolt shorts to the vehicle body it could possibly blow out your rig's final transistor.

One source of homebrew insulating washers is the main output terminals of junk alternators or generators. The washers should be made out of some type of plastic. The best kind of insulating washer has a shoulder around its hole. You drill a hole in the vehicle body, big enough to allow the shoulder to fit through. This holds the bolt away from the metal body.

If you can't find a plastic washer with a shoulder, it is possible to use two flat plastic washers with a little piece of plastic tubing in place of the shoulder. Make sure the plastic tubing is tough enough to not get cut up by the edge of the hole in the vehicle body. It is even possible to home-make plastic washers out of junk plastic jugs and buckets, etc.

You can also use this antenna with a store-bought mount if the bolt on the bottom of the antenna is made to match the mount.

I have talked 30 miles mobile to base on my homemade antenna, using a $20 barefoot rig. Good luck! – Ratchet Jaw

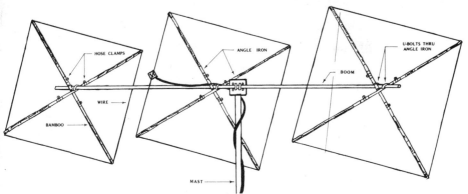

The Quad — Build This 12 db Gain Beam!

How about hoisting this next one up the flagpole—it definitely looks like she'll fly. It is built out of two or more loops of wire that are supported by bamboo or PVC pipe.

Parts List

110 feet of stranded insulated copper wire, 12-14 gauge, to be cut into three separate pieces
One 3" diameter (thick wall) aluminum pipe, 10-14 ft. long
Twenty-four 3" hose clamps
20 ft. of 1" angle aluminum stock
Eight 3" U-bolts, nuts, and lock washers
12 x 12" aluminum (or steel) plate, 1/8" thick
Rubber strips for padding the bamboo
Bamboo (or 1" PVC pipe)
    for driven — 4 pcs., 6 ft long.
    for reflector — 4 pcs., 6 ft. 7 in. long
    for director — 4 pcs., 5 ft. 5 in. long
One plexiglass plate, approx 6 x 6"
One roll nylon twine
Two 1½" U-bolts, nuts and lock washers
One 1½" o.d. galvanized steel pipe, 6 ft. long

The distance between elements can vary from about 5' to 6'9" depending on what size antenna you think you can handle. The shorter the spacing the less gain. The advantage of shorter spacing is in the antenna's compactness and easier maneuverability. The distance between the reflector and the driven element should be a few inches more than between the director and the driven element. For the highest gain use a spacing of 6'9" between reflector and driven and 6'3" between director and driven elements.

Assembly of Our Homebrew Quad Antenna

Step 1— Selecting bamboo. When picking out bamboo, pick thick straight pieces that have no cracked places. Bamboo should be weatherproofed by filling the ends and any cracks with caulking, and painting the whole thing with varnish or marine paint. Bamboo should be roughed up first to allow the sealer to soak in, using rough sandpaper. Apply at least two coats of varnish.

Step 2— Cut ángle aluminum into 3 ft. sections. Drill 2 holes in each piece, one hole 1½" on either side of exact center. These holes must be big enough to fit the U-bolts through.

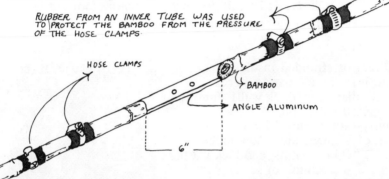

RUBBER FROM AN INNER TUBE WAS USED TO PROTECT THE BAMBOO FROM THE PRESSURE OF THE HOSE CLAMPS.

HOSE CLAMPS

BAMBOO

ANGLE ALUMINUM

6"

Step 3— Clamp bamboo in place on each piece of angle aluminum with hose clamps. If necessary, use rubber padding in between clamps and bamboo for a snug fit. Leave a 6-inch gap between bamboo pieces for U-bolting cross-arms to boom. The distance from tip to tip on each crossarm should be the following:

Reflector	2 cross-arms	13'8"
Driven	2 cross-arms	12'5"
Director	2 cross-arms	11'3"

Keep the cross-arms for each element separate.

Step 4— Making an assembly stand. You'll need to mount the boom up off the ground at least 6½ feet to allow you to put on the cross-arms. This will give you room to spin the quad around while putting on the wires. That lets you be on the ground for that part of the assembly—a much easier way of doing it than being up on a ladder. What we did was take two saw horses and nail an upright to each one. We nailed in a couple of 16-penny nails in the top of each one—that provided a cradle for the boom.

Also, it's good to assemble the quad as near as possible to where it is to be mounted. That will make it much easier to get it up there when the time comes.

Step 5— Mounting crossarms on the boom. After getting the boom up in the air, you can U-bolt on the cross-arms for each element. The pair of cross-arms the right length to make up each element are placed back to back, making the X pattern that supports the wire square that is the element. The U-bolts go around the boom and through the holes in each piece of angle aluminum. It's a good idea to have a little piece of rubber in between the boom and the U-bolts to prevent any slipping caused by the metal on metal contact. Torque down the U-bolt nuts as tight as possible while keeping the cross-arms square to the boom and straight up and down. Also make sure that the cross-arms for each element line up straight with one another.

Step 6— Fastening the wire to the cross-arms. First, you'll need to cut a piece of wire to make each element out of. Cut the following lengths of wire: 38'2"—reflector; 34'10"—driven; 31'4"—director. Remember to keep it straight where each wire goes so as to get the right length of wire on the right set of cross-arms — IT'S IMPORTANT!

The wire can be tied down on the ends of the bamboo about 1"-2" from the ends of the tips with several tight turns of nylon string. Keep the wires tightly strung between the cross-arms without any kinks, loops, or slack. This can be done while standing on the ground and rotating the cross-arms around from top to bottom while fastening on the wire, until you have made a square.

String the wires for the driven element so that the two ends end up in the middle, between the two spreaders. Now twist the two ends of the reflector together. Make sure to scrape any insulation or enamel off the wires and solder the connection. Do the same for the director.

Make sure not to cut any of the wires off when connecting the ends together. Twist together only two inches of each end. Don't connect the wires of the driven element together yet.

Step 7– Hooking up the driven element. Connect each end of the driven element into opposite holes of the plexiglass. This is done by making a loop through the hole and twisting the wire back on itself. Now attach some RG58 or RG8 coax to the driven element's wires. Strip back the coax about 3 to 4

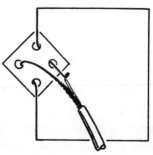

inches and attach the inner conductor of the coax to the end that will be the top of the antenna. Connect the shield side of the coax to the other end of the driven element. Twist together, solder, and tape each connection.

Step 8– Mast to boom mount. Drill the holes in the aluminum or steel plate according to the diagram. Make sure holes are big enough for the U-bolts to fit through. The two U-bolts that attach to the mast will have to be the same size as the mast's diameter. Now mount the plate on the boom at the balance point of the antenna. It should be just behind the driven element. These bolts should be tightened down securely, using lock washers.

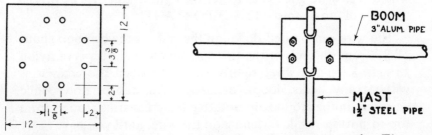

The antenna can now be mounted on the tower or pole. The mast is used between the rotator and the boom.

Quad Gain

2 elements = 9 db
3 elements = 12 db
4 elements = 14 db
5 elements = 17 db

Make sure you check your SWR before settling down to operate. It should be lower than 2. All the ones we've built have had an SWR of 1.3 or better.

Quads are somewhat more susceptible to damage from high winds than other antennas and should be as tightly assembled as possible for long-lasting performance.

You can make this quad with two elements, also. The boom would only have to be 6 feet long. Just leave off the director and mount the driven element and reflector on two opposite ends of the boom. The mast-to-boom plate would be mounted on the center of the boom at the balance point. This antenna is physically much smaller, while only sacrificing about 3db gain. You could also make a higher gain quad by adding more directors and having a longer boom, just so you space them the same as you spaced the other elements. This makes for a longer, bigger antenna.

Putting up a Big Bertha beam   Ear trouble

CHAPTER 11

Emergency Procedures

There are many times when CB is the quickest or the only way to get help in an emergency situation. *You might be the one* to come across a motorist off in a ditch or in need of assistance.

First, determine what kind of assistance you need and how you can best get this assistance. If you are on the interstate or freeway, there will be a lot of mobile stations on the trucker channel. Also, if mechanical assistance such as a wrecker is needed, you may find a local wrecking service monitoring the trucker channel. There may be a Smokey on this channel, too, if you need one.

It might be best to get in touch with a base station that has a land line if you can't get direct assistance.

Channel 9 is the National Emergency and Highway Assistance channel. There are base and mobile stations all over the country that monitor Channel 9 for this purpose. Here is an example of how to get help on Channel 9:

THIS IS ___(call sign)___ AT ___(exact location)___
IN NEED OF ASSISTANCE. IS THERE A BASE STATION ON
THE CHANNEL? OVER.

It's likely that a station will respond to your call with his call sign and ask what he or she can do to help.

If the situation is a life and death emergency, you can get on the air and break for a 10-33.

BREAK. BREAK. BREAK. WE HAVE A 10-33 AT
___(exact location)___ THIS IS ___(call sign)___
REQUESTING ___(police, medical, etc.)___ ASSISTANCE.
OVER.

If you can't make contact on Channel 9, try other channels. After making contact on another channel, you can change to Channel 9 to pass any needed information.

You should stay at the scene until you are no longer needed.

If you hear an emergency situation, you should immediately stop all transmitting and listen to see if the station involved is getting assistance. If another station is already helping out, it is probably best to just listen for awhile to see if it's covered.

In some situations you might have to answer the call for help. In this case, keep all transmissions as short as possible and speak clearly, giving the station your call sign and location.

Write down all information, including:

    Station's call sign
    Exact location of emergency
    Description of emergency
    Type of help needed
    Time

Ask the station to remain at the scene in case there is any further need for communication.

After making any necessary phone calls, let the station know if help is on the way. Stay in contact if possible until help arrives.

It's a good idea to announce the situation on the trucker channel if it is a highway accident.

You shouldn't transmit on any of the 23 channels while you are within a mile of the emergency scene if other stations are passing emergency traffic. You might bleed over onto Channel 9 or any other channel if you are close.

It's a good idea not to use channel 8 or 10 on the highway at all, because you might tend to bleed over onto Channel 9. This goes for skip talkers, too. The main thing is to listen closely and pay good attention.

TEN CODE   Used By CBers

10-1   Receiving poorly
10-2   Receiving well
10-3   Stop transmitting
10-4   OK, message received
10-5   Relay message
10-6   Busy, stand by
10-7   Out of service, leaving air, not working
10-8   In service, subject to call, working well
10-9   Repeat message
10-10 Transmission completed, standing by
10-11 Talking too fast
10-12 Visitors present
10-13 Advise weather/road conditions
10-16 Make pickup at _____
10-17 Urgent business
10-18 Anything for us?
10-19 Nothing for you, return to base
10-20 My location is _____
10-21 Call by telephone
10-22 Report in person to _____
10-23 Stand by
10-24 Completed last assignment
10-25 Can you contact
10-26 Disregard last information
10-27 I am moving to Channel __
10-28 Identify your station
10-29 Time is up for contact
10-30 Does not conform to FCC rules
10-32 I will give you a radio check
10-33 EMERGENCY TRAFFIC AT THIS STATION
10-34 TROUBLE AT THIS STATION HELP NEEDED
10-35 Confidential information
10-36 Correct time is _____
10-37 Wrecker needed at _____
10-38 Ambulance needed at _____
10-39 Your message delivered
10-41 Please tune to Channel _____
10-42 Traffic accident at _____

10-43 Traffic tieup at _____
10-44 I have a message for you (or for _____)
10-45 All units within range please report
10-46 Assist motorist
10-50 Break channel
10-55 Intoxicated driver (DWI)
10-60 What is next message number?
10-62 Unable to copy, use phone
10-63 Network directed to _____
10-64 Network is clear
10-65 Awaiting your next message
10-66 Cancel message
10-67 All units comply
10-68 Repeat message
10-69 Message received
10-70 Fire at _____
10-71 Proceed with transmission in sequence
10-73 Speed trap at_____
10-74 Negative
10-75 You are causing interference
10-77 Negative contact
10-81 Reserve hotel room for ____
10-82 Reserve room for _____
10-84 My telephone number is ___
10-85 My address is _____
10-88 Advise phone number of _____
10-89 Radio repairman needed at_____
10-90 I have TV interference
10-91 Talk closer to mike
10-92 Your transmitter is out of adjustment
10-93 Check my frequency on this channel
10-94 Please give me a long count
10-95 Transmit dead carrier for 5 seconds
10-97 Check test signal
10-99 Mission completed, all units secure
10-100 Restroom stop
10-200 Police needed at _____
73's   Best wishes
88's   Love and kisses

International Morse Code

A · —	1 · — — — —
B — · · ·	2 · · — — —
C — · — ·	3 · · · — —
D — · ·	4 · · · · —
E ·	5 · · · · ·
F · · — ·	6 — · · · ·
G — — ·	7 — — · · ·
H · · · ·	8 — — — · ·
I · ·	9 — — — — ·
J · — — —	0 — — — — —
K — · —	
L · — · ·	
M — —	period. · — · — · —
N — ·	question? · · — — · ·
O — — —	comma, — — · · — —
P · — — ·	dash— — · · · —
Q — — · —	slant bar/ — · · — ·
R · — ·	error · · · · · · · ·
S · · ·	stand by · — · · ·
T —	
U · · —	
V · · · —	
W · — —	
X — · · —	
Y — · — —	
Z — — · ·	

Common Medical Terms

Arrest	A patient whose heart or respiration has stopped.
Arrhythmia	Abnormal heart rhythm.
BP	Blood pressure.
CCU	Coronary Care Unit where serious heart patients are hospitalized.
Code Blue	Cardiac arrest.
Defibrillator	A device which shocks the heart into rhythm.
EKG	Electrocardiogram.
ER	Emergency room.
ICU	Intensive Care Unit, where critically ill patients are hospitalized.
IV	Intravenous, administering fluids intravenously.
MI	Myocardial Infarct: heart attack.
MICU	Mobile Intensive Care Unit.
OB	Obstetrics: childbirth.
OR	Operating room.
Sinus Rhythm	The normal rhythm of the heart.
STAT	Immediately.
Vital Signs	Blood pressure, pulse, breathing rate, temperature.

R-S Reports

Example: Your signal is coming in 5 by 9 here.

Readability

1 - Unreadable
2 - Barely readable
3 - Readable with difficulty
4 - Readable with little difficulty
5 - Perfectly readable

Signal Strength (S-Meter reading)

1 - Barely perceptible
2 - Very weak signal
3 - Weak signal
4 - Fair signal
5 - Fairly good signal
6 - Good signal
7 - Moderately strong signal
8 - Strong signal
9 - Extremely strong signal

International Q-Signals
Used by HAMS and Skip Talkers

QRA	-	Name or handle
QRH	-	Frequency varies
QRL	-	Busy
QRM	-	Interference from other stations
QRN	-	Natural interference - static
QRO	-	Increase transmitter power
QRP	-	Decrease transmitter power
QRQ	-	Transmit faster
QRS	-	Transmit more slowly
QRT	-	Stop transmitting
QRU	-	I have nothing for you
QRV	-	I am ready
QRX	-	Call back later, stand by
QRZ	-	Who is calling me?
QSA	-	Readability
QSB	-	Fading signal
QSL	-	Acknowledge receipt
QSM	-	Repeat the last message
QSP	-	I will relay
QSO	-	Communications with, contact
QSY	-	Change frequency
QSZ	-	Send each word or sentence more than once
QTH	-	Location
QTR	-	Correct time is _____

CHANNEL JIVE (CBers Lingo)

A little help — Extra power
Adios — Leaving the air
Advertising — A marked police car with lights on
Affirmative — Yes
Alligator Station — All mouth and no ears; a big mouth who
    likes to talk and not listen; also, a radio that only transmits
    and does not receive
Anchored modulator — Base station
Appliance operator — A CBer who doesn't know anything about
    his radio; also, a West Coast CB club
Back door — Back door closed, back door seal up
Back door — Last mobile in a line of trucks, watching what's
    coming up from behind
Background — Noise or static on the channel
Back 'em on down — Ending CB conversation; also, slow down
Back 'em on out — Ending CB conversation
Back 'em up — Ending CB conversation; also, back up truck
Back stroke — Return trip   also use Rebound, Back side
Bagging — Police catching speeders
Barefoot — Running without a kicker
Barley pop — Beer
Barn — Truck garage
Base — Stationary rig; also, a rig used as a base station
Base Station — Rig at fixed location
Basement — Channel 1
Bean store — Restaurant or road stop where food is served
Bear — Police
Bear in the air — Police in helicopter or airplane
Bear in the bushes — Police hiding
Bear bait — Someone driving fast without a radio, near police
Bear bite — Speeding ticket
Bear cave, cage, den — Police station
Bear's lair — Police station

Bear story — Police location report

Beating the bushes — Vehicle driving ahead of a group and going just enough over the speed limit (but not fast enough to get a ticket) to bring out any hidden police cars to investigate. Lead vehicle watching for speed traps.

Beaver — small, furry, large-toothed animal that lives in the water.

Better cool it — Slow down or stop transmitting

Better half — Your wife or husband

Big brother — Police

Big Ten Four, Four Roger for Sure, Ten Roger Four, Ten Roger D., Four Ten Roger, Roger Roger, Roger Dodger — Yeah

Big Dummy — Affectionate truck driver term; good buddy

Big ears — Good receiver

Bird — Thunderbird

Bird in the air — Unidentified helicopter or airplane

Bit on the seat of the britches — Got a ticket

Black and White — Police car

Black and White CBer — Police with CB

Black water — Coffee

Bleeding over — Station spilling over onto nearby channels, usually caused by overmodulation

Blinkin' Winkin' — School bus

Blood box — Ambulance

Blowin' Smoke — Coming in loud and clear (making my rig smoke)

Bob-tail — Semi-tractor running without a trailer.

Bodacious — Loud, sounds good

Boat anchor — A big old radio

Bootlegging — Using another station other than your own, illegal station

Bootleggers — Skip talkers' club

Boots, shoes, galoshes — Kickers

Bottle popper — Beverage truck

Break — Call a station

Break, Break; Breakity Break; Breaker Break; Breaker Broke Break, etc. — What you say to get on a channel

Breaking up — Your signal is cutting on and off. "Mercy sakes! Yer breaking up all over the place."

Bring it on, Bring yourself on, Brought it on — Go ahead, it's clear

Brown bottles — Beer

Brought yerself on up — Put the hammer down and come this way

Bubble gum machine — Vehicle with flashing lights or revolving lights on top of the car

Bucket mouth — CBer who won't shut up

Bull jockey — Someone who shoots a lot of bull on CB

Bumper lane — Passing lane on a 4-lane road

Burning up my ears — Got a good signal

Bushels — half tons, one thousand pounds

Candy man — FCC man

Camera — Hand held radar unit

CB Land — The land where CB communications happen and folks on CB meet

Catch a few "z's" — Get some sleep

Charlie — The FCC   also use Uncle Charlie

Chicken box — CB radio

Chicken coop — Truck weighing station

Chicken inspector — Weigh station inspector

Choo-choo train — Semi hauling two trailers

Clean — No Smokeys "The 4-wheeler on the grass is clean."

Clean shot – Road is clear of Smokeys and there are good road conditions

Clear, off and clear – Signing off

Come back – Say it, or say it again

Come on, bring it on – Go ahead

Convoy – Group of travelers trucking together

Cotton-picker – Fellow CBer

Copying the mail – Listening to folks talk on the channel

County Mountie – County sherriff

Definitely, definatory – Sure will

Diesel car – Semi-tractor truck

Diesel digit – Channel 19

Dime channel – Channel 10

Dog – Greyhound bus

Dog biscuits – db, decibels

Doing it to it – Hammer down, traveling right along not wasting any time

"Waddya mean, where's my ears?"

Double "L" – Land line, telephone

Double nickel – 55 miles per hour (approximately)

Doubled – Two stations transmitted at the same time

Don't feed the bears – Don't get busted "There's a Smokey on up ahead, so slow down–ya don't want to feed the bears."

Draggin' wagon – Wrecker

Dummy – Empty cop car, parked as a decoy

Dusted your britches – Transmitted at the same time

Ears – Antenna "You got yer ears on?"

Eatum-up stop – Restaurant or truck stop

Eights, Eighty-eights – Hugs and kisses, good wishes, a good number

Emergency vehicle – Ambulance, fire, or rescue vehicle (usually with lights on)

Eye in the sky – Airplane checking speed

Eleven meters – CB band

Fat load – Overweight load

Feed the bears – Pay a ticket

Fifty dollar lane – Left-most lane, or passing lane

Final – Last transmission; also, final power amplifier tube or transistor

Flag waver – Highway worker

Flat side — Horizontal polarization; also, sleep
Flip, Flip-flop, Flipper — Return trip; also, U-turn
    "Catch you on the flipper, good buddy."
Fluff stuff — snow
Fly in the sky — Aircraft, possibly Smokeys
Foot-warmer — Linear amp
Forty-weight — Coffee
Front door — First mobile in line, letting everyone know what's
    coming up
Funny Candy Company — FCC
Give a shout — Give a call
Git back — Go ahead, over
Going horizontal — Lying down, going to sleep; also, switching
    to horizontal polarization
Going thataway — Signing off; also, headed away from the
    Home 20
Going thisaway — Headed toward the Home 20
Gone, we gone — Signing off, clearing channel
Good Buddy — Fellow CBer
Good numbers — Best regards and good wishes   "Threes and
    eights and all them good numbers on ya."
Got a copy? — Do you hear me?
Got your ears on? — Do you hear me?
Grass — Median strip or along side of road
Green light — Clear road on up ahead
Green stamps — Money (1 stamp=$1); also, issuing tickets
    "Smokey's collecting green stamps from a 4-wheeler up there."
Green stamp road — Toll road
Ground clouds — Fog
Guarantold you — I'm telling you the truth
Guy — Fellow trucker
Haircut Place — Low clearance overpass
Handle — CB nickname   "What's your handle?"
Hammer — Accelerator pedal
Harvey Wallbanger — Reckless driver
Holding onto your mud flaps — Driving right behind you
Hole in the wall — Tunnel
Horizontal, flat side — Go to bed; also, horizontally polarized
Home Twenty — Location of your home
Honey bear — Female state trooper
How about it? — Come back; say it; we're calling you
In a short — Soon
In a short short — Real soon
Invitations — Police traffic citations, tickets
Keep 'em between the ditches — Have a safe trip
Keep the shiny side up and the greasy side down — Have a safe
    trip
Kicker — Linear amplifier
Land line — telephone
Linear — Linear amplifier, illegal amplifier of signal
Little box — Mobile linear
Local yokel — Local police
Local Smokel — Local or city police
Looking thataway — Looking for a Smokey report   "How's it
    looking thataway, good buddy?"
Loose board-walk — Bumpy road
Making the trip — You're getting out, I can hear you
Mama bear — Policewoman
Marijuana taxi — Fully outfitted police cruiser
Marker — Mile marker, milepost on the highway

"Wall-to-wall bears"

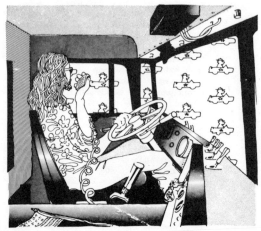

May Day — International emergency distress call
Mercy sakes! — Wow!
Modjitating — Talking
Motor motor — Travel
Motion lotion — Gasoline, diesel
Mud — Coffee
Nap trap — Rest area; also, motel
Negatory — No
Nickel channel — Channel 5
On the peg — Legal speed limit
On the side — End of talking, but will be monitoring the channel
Over your shoulder — Behind you
Over — End of transmission, your turn
Patch — Town
Peanut butter in the ears — Someone who can't hear too good
   has this problem
Peanut whistle — Low powered station: also, station with no
   kicker
Pedal to the metal, hammer down — Accelerator floored
Plain wrapper — An unmarked police car   "You've got a Smokey
   in a plain brown wrapper on your backdoor."
Picture taker (Brush your teeth and comb your hair) — Radar
Pictures — Radar
Porcupine — Mobile with lots of antennas
Portable chicken coop, weight watcher — Dept. of Transporta-
   tion mobile weighing station
Pokey — Jail
Portable parking lot — Auto carrier
Portable stockyards — Cattle truck
Post — Mile marker
Pounds — Watts, notches on the "S" meter   "Yer putting
   about nine pounds on my meter."
Pull the big switch — Turn off the CB, go off the air
Put an eyeball on ya — See you in person
Put my teeth up for the night, go 10-7 — Sign off
QSL card — postcard with call letters and handle exchanged by
   CBers
Radio check — Asking how your rig sounds: "How about a
   radio check?"
Ratchet jaw — Someone who talks a lot on the radio

Reading the mail — Listening to the channel

Rest 'em up stop — Rest stop

Rig — CB radio; also, big truck or vehicle

Rock — Radio crystal

Rocking chair — That's what you're sitting in when you're in contact with mobiles ahead and behind you

Roger roller-skate — A four-wheeler going in and out fast between trucks

Roller-skate — A small car, such as a compact or import

Rolling roadblock — Vehicle going under the speed limit and holding up traffic

"S" unit — "S" meter reading increment

Shoes — Linear amplifier

Sailboat fuel — Running on an empty gas tank; also, no load in trailer

Seeing eye dog — Device which detects police radar

Seat covers — Passengers, usually ladies

Shake the trees and rake the leaves — Lead vehicle watch ahead and rear vehicle watch behind, in a group of vehicles in CB contact

Shake the bushes, run the front door, go on out ahead — First vehicle in a group drives just fast enough to bring out any police along the road, but not fast enough to get a ticket

Show-off lane — Left hand lane

Skating rink — Slippery road

Skip land — Any place farther away than 60 miles

Skip talker — A CBer who talks long distances

Slider — V.F.O., a device used to make a rig tune across all the channels, in between them, and then some

Smokey, Smokey the Bear — Cop

Smokey report — Location of Smokey the Bear in the direction you're headed

Smokey's got ears — Cop with CB radio

Sounding choice — Got a good-sounding signal

Smoke it on — Go ahead, over, bring it on

Squawk box — CB radio

Suicide sleeper — Truck with sleeper over cab

Super skate — Sports car

Sweet thing — Lady on the channel

Taking pictures — Police using radar

Thermos bottle — Tank truck

Three 3's, 73's — Good luck, best wishes

CAUTION: DON'T FEED THE BEARS!

PICTURES TAKEN NO WAITING!

COMB YOUR TEETH AND BRUSH YOUR HEAD.

Ten fer — Over
Tiajuana taxi — State trooper car with lights, sirens, etc.
Train station — Court with high guilty rate
Two wheeler — Motorcycle or bicycle
Truck 'em easy — Take it easy driving
Twins — Dual antennas
Twister — Highway interchange
TVI — Television interference

Vertical — Vertical ground plane antenna
Vertical side — Vertical polarization

Walking all over you — Another louder station is covering up
   your signal
Walking tall — Good sounding signal
Walking the dog — Talking over a long distance
Wallpaper — QSL cards, exchanged by CBers, that have their
   call sign, handle, and location printed on them
Wall to wall and tree top tall — Loud and clear signal
Wall to wall bears — Lots of Smokeys
Weight watcher — Mobile truck weighing station
Whoop! Mercy Sakes — Oh, wow!
What am I putting on you? — What does your "S" meter read?
   How well can you hear me?
What about ya? — Are you there?
Willy Weaver — Drunken driver

X-Band — Radar frequency Smokeys use
X-ray machine — Radar

Yeah four — 10-4, yes

Z's — Sleep

"Hey . . . ah . . . Front Door, what state we in, ... ?"

Index

Catch Ya On The Flip !

If you're ever passin' by our 20 in the hills of Tennessee, give a shout for that old Farm Base on that one nickel channel. We'll be glad to ratchet jaw with ya for sure! So 3's and 8's and all them good numbers on ya. Ya'll have a good day today and a better day tomorrow. We're on the side !